KINGDOM PARK

KINGDOM PARK

A walk with the Master from the Cross shaped Gate to the Father's House

GLORIA KEARNEY

AMBASSADOR INTERNATIONAL
GREENVILLE, SOUTH CAROLINA & BELFAST, NORTHERN IRELAND

www.ambassador-international.com

Kingdom Park

A walk with the Master from the Cross shaped Gate to the Father's House

Copyright 2010 - Gloria Kearney
All rights reserved

ISBN: 978-1-935507-54-3

Design & Printed by Bethel Solutions

Ambassador International
Emerald House
427 Wade Hampton Blvd
Greenville, SC 29609, USA

Ambassador Books and Media
The Mount
2 Woodstock Link
Belfast, BT6 8DD, Northern Ireland, UK

www.ambassador-international.com

The colophon is a trademark of Ambassador

This book is dedicated to my newest granddaughter,
Charlotte Rose.
Her smile lights up the room!
May the smile of Jesus light up her life.

My thanks

To my wonderful family who happily put up with scrappy meals and an untidy house so that Mum can write – better days are coming, folks!

To my fabulous friends and prayer partners, Gwen, Lavinia and Pat, who encourage me by listening patiently to my poems and Master stories – see you on Friday, girls!

To my church family at Ballynahinch Baptist who support me by buying the books and allowing me to share some of the pieces in the services – your encouragement is much appreciated.

To the team at Ambassador International – thank you for agreeing to publish another of my little books – may God bless you richly.

To the Master who has faithfully walked with me for many years – what a journey it has been! Your goodness and mercy has followed me all the days of my life.

Other books by Gloria Kearney

Sing in the Shadow
Special Moments
A Place Prepared
Sunrise to Sunset
The Voice in the Laburnum Tree
A Sparrow's Tale (with Lavinia Abrol)

Gloria Kearney can be contacted at
gloriakearney@hotmail.com

Sing in the Shadow and Special Moments are out of print.
The other titles are available from Gloria Kearney.

CONTENTS

FOREWORD

Kingdom Park is the third book in a series of 'Master' stories. In the first, 'Special Moments', the Master leads His child through the rooms in the Father's house, teaching valuable lessons in each room. 'Sunrise to Sunset' describes a walk with the Master beside still waters, visiting Green Pastures, the Boatshed and the Marina along the way.

In Kingdom Park, the scene changes to the mountains and valleys of the Father's kingdom. The Master shows His child Freedom Road, the Grace House, Spirit Reservoir and the Golden Strand. His Presence brings comfort and strength in Shadow Valley and the Cave of Depression and enables His child to face the final Winter Season.

It is my prayer that as you follow the journey with the Master, you too will know the nearness of His Presence, hear the whisper of His voice and sense His clear direction for your path.

Gloria

*Small is the gate
and narrow the road
that leads to life.*

Matthew ch 7 v 13

CHAPTER 1
LAY IT DOWN

"Have you been inside?" I asked the young man who was sitting on a low wall at the side of the road.

"Inside the Park?" he asked. I nodded and he smiled broadly. "Oh I've been inside alright! I live in Kingdom Park."

"You're the first person I've ever spoken to who actually lived there," I exclaimed and sat down beside him on the wall.

"I've met some of your neighbours on my journey," I went on, "but, to be honest, I was afraid to speak to them. They gave me disapproving looks as they passed by and they looked so serious and always seemed to be in such a hurry......"

A look of sadness and regret flitted over his face.

"Yes," he agreed, "some of my neighbours are a bit difficult to talk to but they're not all like that."

"What is it really like?" I asked. "I've been walking for ages beside the boundary wall but so far I haven't found the way in and I can't see over the wall."

"Oh, it's a great place to live – I would say it's the only place to live!" he replied enthusiastically. "There's plenty to see and do. It's never boring – always something new and exciting. Of course the best thing about it is the opportunity to get to know the Master."

"I've read about Him," I said with a sigh. "He seems to be amazing. Do you know Him well?"

My companion looked across at Kingdom Park and said with what sounded like longing in His voice,

"Not as well as I would like to know Him."

"Would you like to see the entrance gate?" he continued. "It's not too far from here, just around the corner."

I nodded my assent and followed him down the road. We had just rounded the corner when he stopped me and pointed to a gap in the wall.

"That's the entrance," he said proudly. "Come on in, everyone's welcome."

"That's the entrance?" I asked in utter astonishment. "But it's so small and narrow. I was expecting something much more imposing than that – a wide entrance with electric gates, maybe, or a gate-lodge with guards on duty. And there should be big signs on the road to mark the entrance. Surely there must be another way in?"

"No," my companion assured me, "that's the only entrance in the entire boundary wall, the only way in to Kingdom Park."

I was curious to see what lay on the other side of the narrow gate so I approached and began to go through when suddenly I was stopped in my tracks – my knapsack got stuck and no matter how I tried, I couldn't get it through the gate. My friend, who had told me that his name was Rescuer, didn't seem surprised at all that I couldn't get through.

"It's your knapsack that's the problem," he said gently. "You've got to lay it down before you can go through."

"Lay down my knapsack?" I was horrified at the very suggestion.

"I couldn't do that –my whole life is in the knapsack. I can't remember a time when I didn't have the knapsack on my back."

"But don't you understand?" Rescuer asked. "That knapsack you've been carrying all your life is your sin. That's why you can't get in – you can't bring the sin with you."

I turned to face him. I was not only horrified but deeply offended.

"How dare you!" I shouted. "How dare you say that I've been

carrying sin around with me! I've lived a good life……… I've done lots of good things……….. There's no way I'm laying down my knapsack!"

Still muttering angrily under my breath I turned away from the gate and stomped off down the road again but the further I walked away from the gate, the more aware I became of the weight on my back.

"How strange," I thought, "my knapsack has never bothered me before. It feels heavier and more uncomfortable…………"

I adjusted the straps and struggled on but I kept hearing Rescuer's voice in my ear,

"It's your sin…………. It's your sin……….."

I stopped some of the other travellers on the road and told them about the problem I was having and how my knapsack was getting heavier and heavier. They assured me that it was all in my imagination and that their knapsacks were lightweight and easy to carry. They laughed loudly when I told them what Rescuer had said about the knapsack being sin.

"Oh you don't want to listen to that nonsense," said one of them. "Walk with us for a while and we'll help you to forget about the knapsack."

So I walked with them and they did their best to help me forget. They played music on their ipods to distract me, they gave me tablets to help with the pain, they told jokes to make me laugh but all their efforts were in vain. Soon I was bent double, crying because of the weight of my burden and I knew I had to go back to the gate.

As I slowly and painfully made my way round the last bend in the road, I saw something that I hadn't noticed on my first visit to the gate. The narrow entrance was shaped like a cross.

Rescuer came to meet me and he led me to the cross.
"You rushed off before I could explain," he said. "The only

entrance to Kingdom Park is through the cross of Jesus. He took all our sin and died so that He could offer us forgiveness. In fact, He actually became sin for us…………."

I shifted uneasily as I thought of some of the things I had been carrying around in my knapsack and suddenly a wave of sorrow rose up from deep within me.

"He became my sin…………. No, no………….. how could that be?"

I threw myself at the foot of the cross.

"Forgive me Jesus……………… forgive me," I cried out and even as I thought the words to speak them, the weight of the knapsack fell from my back and instantly I found myself on the other side of the gate, in Kingdom Park.

As I turned to look back at the cross, a deep well of joy flooded my whole being and for the first time in my life I knew and received real forgiveness, grace, peace and love. Then a voice spoke my name and a hand touched my head. In that moment I understood the longing in Rescuer's voice – I wanted to know the One who had called my name – no, it was stronger than that – I yearned to know Him. He was the Master and from that moment on, would be my Master.

IMMANUEL

Tis miracle enough
To think of Bethlehem,
When God the Lord Almighty
Came to the sons of men.
He took the form of man –
A child of humble birth
And lived in blameless purity,
On this wicked, sinful earth.

A miracle greater still
Is that of Calvary,
When God the Lord Almighty,
In Jesus died for me.
He took my sin upon Him
As if it were His own,
Went through pain and isolation,
For my sin to atone.

A miracle so wondrous –
How could it ever be?
Is that of the Lord Almighty,
Immanuel – God in me.
He by His Spirit dwells
Within my heart today,
And promises to give His strength,
And peace and joy always.

DID HEAVEN'S COURTS SEEM EMPTY?

Did Heaven's courts seem empty
When the Son came down to earth?
Did His leaving cast a shadow
On the joy of Jesus' birth?

Did the angels, whose amazing song
With joy and wonder filled the air,
Miss the presence of the Lord of Glory –
Were they sad He wasn't there?

Did heavenly golden streets so bright
Lose some lustre on that night?
Could the crystal sea no more reflect
The One who clothed Himself in light?

Was there a sharp intake of breath
From mighty seraphim,
And did the choirs just miss a beat
At the thought of losing Him?

And did the Father break His heart,
And did the Spirit grieve
The breaking of the Three – in- One,
When Jesus had to leave.

The saddest partings here on earth
Can never be compared
To the sorrow that the Godhead knew
For salvation to be shared.

For if He hadn't come to earth
And died to show God's love
Then we could never live with Him
Forevermore in Heaven above.

So Father, when I say goodbyes
When I feel empty in my heart,
Remind me that You know the pain
And remind me that we'll never part.

CHAPTER 2
LEARNING

Life on the other side of the gate was rather different. I wasn't sure if it was just my imagination or not, but the sky seemed bluer, the air seemed purer and the grass greener. I had often felt alone and incomplete as I followed the path outside but now the Presence of the Master accompanied me and for the first time in my life, I felt whole.

I stood for a moment and just gazed at my surroundings. Kingdom Park was a very beautiful place – gently sloping valleys led to tree-clad hills and far away in the distance I could just make out the outline of snow-capped mountains. Sparkling lakes nestled in the hills and rivers wound their lazy way through the valleys.

"What is this place?" I asked. "What is Kingdom Park?"

"The Father, the Great King of Kings, has an amazing plan for the world He created," the Master began.

"Oh," I interrupted, "I've heard people talk about the Great King – sometimes they call Him the Creator or the Supreme Being. He's very powerful and many people are afraid of Him."

"Here in Kingdom Park," the Master said, "we call Him 'Father.'"

"I can understand You calling Him Father but I'm not sure that I should," I replied. "It seems a bit irreverent."

"It would delight His heart to hear you call Him Father," the Master assured me. "When you came in through the Gate, by the way of My Cross, you became family and that gave you the right to call Him Father."

I walked along in silence for a while, trying to absorb the idea of addressing the Great King as 'Father' and then realised that the Master was continuing His explanation of Kingdom Park.

"The Father's plan is to bring everything under His reign and His rule. The whole plan is centred around the Cross. Everything before the Cross points forward to it and everything after it springs from it. When you enter Kingdom Park you become part of that plan to bring the Father's Kingdom to the earth."

My heart sank at His words……….. I knew so little about the Kingdom……………. The plan seemed so immense. I looked at the Master in dismay.

"I'm not sure about all of this. How could I ever play a part in such a huge plan? I have no idea what to do! What if I fail?"

The Master put His hand out to silence my question.

"You just have to follow Me," He said.

"But I don't even know how to do that!" I cried. "Will someone teach me what to do?"

The Master took my hand and placed in it a book.

"I will teach you what to do. This Book contains My words and the Father's words. It was inspired by the Great Spirit – it will tell you what to do and how to behave."

I gazed in awe at the Book in my hand. I was holding the very words of God. I was so excited that I sat down there and then by the side of the road and began to read. The Master waited patiently while I searched its pages. My excitement quickly turned to dismay.

"It's…….. uh………. a bit difficult…….. isn't it?" I said at last, reluctant to offend the Master but rather disappointed to find that I couldn't understand it. There seemed to be long lists of rules and accounts of gory battles! Was this what the Kingdom was all about?

"I think you may have started in the wrong place!" he said with a smile. "Some of My earliest followers wrote My story – why not start there?"

"Oh I would love to read Your story," I replied, my enthusiasm building again.

"It's also a good idea to ask the Great Spirit for help when you read the Book," added the Master. "After all, He inspired its writing so He would be able to help you understand it."

"That sounds like a good idea," I replied. "The only problem is that I don't know how to do that either! I don't seem to know very much about anything!"

"There is a lot to learn in Kingdom Park," the Master agreed, "but don't be discouraged. You have the rest of your life to learn. As long as you live as a pilgrim in this kingdom, you will continue learning – learning to live in relationship with Us and with your fellow pilgrims, learning to spread the good news of the kingdom to those who live on the other side of the Gate. Yes there is a lot to learn."

Then, to my great surprise, he took out what looked like a weapon and placed it in my other hand. I noticed that engraved along its length was a single word, 'Prayer'.

"That's what you use if you need help in the Kingdom," he said.

"But Master," I protested, "it's a weapon!"

"Oh didn't I mention that we're in a battle?" He replied with a smile. "The Prayer weapon is really useful for fighting against the

Enemy. He has sworn to destroy the Father's Kingdom and has many minions who fight at his side."

Now I was really worried! I didn't like the sound of this enemy of the Kingdom and wasn't even sure if I would recognise him or his minions. The Master seemed to know what I was thinking and reassured me.

"Oh you'll know when the Enemy attacks you. His mission is to steal and kill and destroy so if anything attempts to steal your joy or kill your relationship with Me or destroy the work you will do in the Kingdom, then you will know that the Enemy has come against you."

He then produced a shield and strapped it firmly to my arm. It was big enough to completely cover me and, like the Prayer weapon, was engraved with a name – Faith.

"Your Shield of faith will protect you from his attacks and the more you study the Book and use the Prayer weapon, the stronger your shield will become."

At that moment, what looked like fiery arrows flew in my direction. Instinctively I held out my huge shield and the arrows struck it and fell to the ground without harming me. When the attack ceased, I examined the arrows and discovered that they too bore names – Doubt, Fear and Unbelief.

"It really works," I whispered to the Master. I was still rather shaken by the attack but relieved that now I knew what to do.

"The Enemy will use those arrows again and again," the Master told me, "and Faith is the only thing that will stand against them."

"One thing I haven't told you," He continued with a smile, "the outcome of the battle has already been decided. The Enemy was defeated at the Cross but as long as you walk in Kingdom Park and try to serve Me, he will come against you."

So I set out along the path before me, the Book of the Kingdom in my hand, my Prayer weapon at the ready and the Shield of Faith covering me. I felt equipped for the journey now.

"You must pay a visit to the Armoury in My Father's House," the Master said. "You'll find other armour there – be sure to wear it every day."

And then he raised His voice and His words rang out like a clarion call,

"Don't ever forget – the Battle has been won!"

Take up the shield of faith.
Ephesians ch 6 v 16

THE MUSTARD SEED

I've got it here Lord – can You see?
All the faith that's in my heart.
So small it makes me feel ashamed,
Not much, I know – but it's a start.

Yes, that's it – tucked deep inside.
It doesn't seem too good to me.
A faith so small, so poor, so weak –
How ineffective it must be.

Oh how I long for greater faith
Believing You for bigger things,
Rising over fear and doubt,
A faith that soars on eagle's wings.

A faith that knocks on Heaven's gates
That boldly walks up to the throne,
Faith to take You at Your word
And make Your promises my own.

But all I've got is this poor thing –
The tiniest grain of mustard seed.
With trembling hand I hold it out
And vow to follow where You lead.

And then I seem to hear You say
"It only takes a tiny grain,
Give it to me and you will see
The mountains moving once again.

Don't try to measure up your faith,
I'll use it – whether great or small.
Focus instead upon My mighty power –
Am I not King of Kings and Lord of all?"

*He calls His own sheep by name
and leads them out.*
John ch 10 v 3

I walked a pleasant path, smooth beneath my feet, straight and level. The hedgerows on either side were gently scented, now and then a bird sang its song to Heaven in a nearby tree and the summer sun warmed my hands and face.

I stepped out confidently, sure of the path I was taking and quietly pleased to know that I was doing the Master's will, happy to be busy in His service. I followed the path around a bend and came to a fork in the road. Which way should I take? I shouted back to the Master and thought I saw His arm point to the road on the right so I took that turning.

It wasn't long before I realised that I was in trouble. The smooth firm path gave way to a muddy swamp and my feet were trapped.

"Help, Lord!" I cried out in my distress and instantly He was there at my side.

"Oh Child, you do get into some difficult places," He said as He gently took my hands and guided me out of the muddy swamp.

"I think it's time we had a talk together," He continued as He tenderly wiped my dirty feet and brought me back to the fork in the road.

"I don't think I'm going to like this," I whispered but allowed Him to set me down on the grass at the edge of the path.

"Oh you have nothing to fear, Child," He smiled. "My love is upon you, I see that your heart desires only to serve Me. I know how hard you are trying to please Me and I'm watching over you as you follow the path."

I looked into His face, saw only love in His gaze and that gave me courage to ask a question that had been in my heart for ages.

"Why do I keep making mistakes and getting stuck?"

His reply was instant.

"There's a very simple explanation – a basic problem in our relationship. You're walking out in front, you're going on ahead."

"But I thought that was what You wanted," I cried. "You told me You had work for me to do, You gave me gifts to equip me. Didn't You want me to get on with it?"

"Ah…… but what was your very first instruction at the beginning of this journey?" He asked.

I thought for a moment and then realisation flooded in and my face flamed with embarrassment.

"You told me to follow You," I whispered.

He took my hand and looked intently into my eyes as He spoke, emphasising each word with a little pressure of His fingers on mine.

"If you don't let Me go first, you can't follow Me. That's why you miss My instructions so often. You're striding out in front, then when you don't know the way, you have to turn round and shout back to Me. It just doesn't work that way."

He pulled me to my feet and stepped in front of me.

"Now try it My way," He urged.

So once more I set out on the path, the correct path this time and I practised following the Master. I adjusted my pace to His and found it was much more comfortable walking at the pace He set. My feet weren't so sore, my limbs weren't so weary. And when we came to a fork in the road, I didn't even have to ask which way to go – I could see Him just in front and I simply followed where He led.

"Oh this is so much better," I called out and gave a little skip of joy.

The Master smiled and nodded.

"Yes," He said, "it's definitely best to let me go first. You do have a bit of a problem with 'letting Me', don't you?" He continued.

"Whatever do You mean?" I enquired.

"Well, Child, you have an independent spirit. You're inclined to do things on your own, in your own way. You know you are competent, so you just forget to ask for My direction, My will, My word."

Once again my head bowed in shame as I recognised the truth

of His words.

"You don't find it easy even to let Me love you. Sometimes when I send someone to show you My love, you push them away. As for sitting still long enough to let Me hold or comfort you……….." He broke off and looked at me with a twinkle of amusement in His eye and we both laughed for we knew how hard it was for me to sit still!

We walked side by side for a long time that day as the Master pointed out other places where I needed to 'let Him'…… I needed to stop talking so much and 'let Him' speak to me. He had so many wonderful things to share with me but I rarely heard them, rarely listened to His voice.

I needed to 'let Him' be for me what He wanted to be – sometimes a gentle shepherd, sometimes a warrior king. I needed to 'let Him' fill me with His Spirit, with His energising power instead of relying on my own strength. As we journeyed on, I endeavoured to tune my ear to His voice and each time I tried to step ahead of the Master, I heard His gentle whisper in my ear.

"Let Me………."

COME. FOLLOW

You said, "Come, follow,"
And I came.
The road was unfamiliar
Difficult,
The corners blind,
The gradient steep,
Yet still I came.
For I had heard Your voice,
And it was sweet to me,
So gladly I obeyed
Your servant I would be,
But I could visualize
    The sacrifice,
        The wood,
            The fire,

And shrank from what the knife would do,
Yet journeyed,
With faith and fear and doubt and joy
All intermingled in my heart.
The road led to the mountain-top
The place of sacrifice prepared,
The knife was raised,
And poised to strike –
My hand was stayed –
And only then I saw the ram.

"This sacrifice is not required," You said,
"I only asked to know your heart.
Now I have seen you follow Me,
And give to me that precious part,
Security and future hope –
Tied down, ready for the fire.
Now see the ram – held here for you
I give you back your heart's desire."

You said, "Come, follow,"
And I came.

So if the Son sets you free,
  you will be free indeed.

John ch 8 v 36

CHAPTER 4
LEAVING TRADITION ROAD

Having spent some time walking in Kingdom Park, it was hard to imagine that I had ever lived anywhere else. It was an amazing place, stretching as far as the eye could see and each bend in the road opened up new vistas, new delights to thrill the soul. It was criss-crossed by many paths and it was difficult to choose which way to go.

Eventually I followed a group of pilgrims who were walking purposefully along a path on my right. I fell into step with them and listened to their conversations for a while as I looked ahead to see what sort of road I was following.

It had been laid out straight ahead, like an ancient Roman road and had obviously been well maintained. The grass on either side had been recently mown and the road itself had been swept clean of any fallen leaves or litter. A neat wooden fence backed by wire had been erected on either side.

"I think I've made a good choice," I thought. "This road looks safe to me."

My thoughts were interrupted by one of my fellow pilgrims who had turned round to speak to me.

"We've found that it's best if you walk in the middle of the road," he informed me.

I looked ahead and realised that the group I had seen were indeed walking carefully in the middle of the road and were pulling each other back into line if anyone broke away from the centre. It was on the tip of my tongue to ask why it was the best place to walk but he was an imposing gentleman and had obviously been in Kingdom Park much longer than I had so I bit back my question and meekly moved over to follow the others.

We walked along quite happily for a while and I had just begun to make friends with the young woman who was walking in front of me when another gentleman at the front of the group began to sing a song of praise to the King. Everyone joined in and because I knew the song, I did too. My heart lifted in worship as I looked around at the beauty of Kingdom Park. I had always enjoyed singing and began to add a line of harmony to the song.

Instantly the man at the front stopped singing and began to walk towards me. One by one the other pilgrims stopped singing too and the song died away. The gentleman looked sternly at me and announced,

"We only sing in unison on this path."

My face coloured with embarrassment but I knew in my heart how much richness some harmony could add to a song so this time I dared to ask a question.

"Can you tell me why? Don't you think a little harmony would add life and colour to your praise?"

He drew himself up to a great height and in a tone which defied any argument said,

"You don't understand. We have always sung in unison. The King wouldn't want it any other way. That's the way it has always been and that's the way it will remain!"

With that he marched back to the front of the line and started up the song again. I joined in but my heart was no longer in it and I began to wonder just what sort of path I was following.

As the journey continued I became more and more unhappy.

Now and then I caught glimpses of another path and heard snatches of song from the pilgrims who were travelling there and I was sure I could hear harmony being sung. But I couldn't work out how to join it – the neat fences hemmed me in on both sides.

"Master where are You?" I asked and just as before, He was at my side in a moment.

"I'm so unhappy," I cried. "I know Kingdom Park is a wonderful place but I don't fit in. The other pilgrims don't seem to like me very much. And what is this path I'm following?"

"Well, Child," He replied quietly, "the path you are following is called Tradition Road. The pilgrims don't mean to make you unhappy – it's just that you're trying to do things differently and they don't like change. In fact, they really believe that the King doesn't like change either."

"Oh," I exclaimed, "that's not what it says in the Book. I read just the other day that the King is changing us from glory to glory."

The Master smiled.

"Yes, little one," He said, "the King's heart for you is that you will be transformed."

"I don't think I will be transformed very much if I stay on this path. Can I walk somewhere else?" I asked.

"It is rather difficult to leave Tradition Road," the Master said in a serious tone. "The further you travel, the more narrow the road and the higher the fences on either side. The best plan of action is to climb the fence now. Take my hand and I'll help you."

It was a tough choice – although I had been unhappy, I had been safe. There was no danger of slipping over the edge with a stout fence to protect me. I had not had to think for myself – there was a certain security in simply doing what I was told to do.

But just then I heard a snatch of song from the path nearby and so beautiful was the harmony that I put my hand in the Master's hand and began to climb the fence. It was a hard climb and near the top, strands of barbed wire caught at my clothes as though the very road itself didn't want to let me go. With a final tug and a determined effort, I reached the top and threw myself over.

With my hand still in the Master's I ran to the other path. I noticed that there were no fences on its edges and my heart began to beat a little faster. This road would not be so safe and I would need to guard my feet but the singing thrilled my heart and the pilgrims reached out to draw me into their company. I added my harmony and no one told me to stop. I saw a smile on the Master's face as the pilgrims sent their song of worship heavenward.

"What's the name of this path?" I asked a fellow pilgrim when the song ended.

"This is Freedom Road," he replied and I thought of the way the Master had helped me over the fence as I remembered other words I had read in the Book,

"He whom the Son sets free is free indeed."

ANNA

Anna knew how to stay in His Presence,
In the Temple, day after day.
Her life was a life full of worship,
She knew how to fast and to pray.

Anna's feet never walked through the veil,
She couldn't see the lamb being slain,
Far back in the court of the women,
She waited, again and again.

And God came, from the Holy of Holies,
Walked on through the Holy Place,
Passed the men as they stood in the Temple,
Chose to meet Anna face to face.

And she knew the sound of His voice,
Heard it clearly, despite all the din,
Had the courage to speak out the words
That the Spirit prompted within.

Oh meet with me, as with Anna,
Speak to me, Oh my Lord, face to face.
Bring me day after day to Your Presence,
Whisper words full of truth and of grace.

In all your ways acknowledge Him
and He will make your paths straight.

Proverbs ch 3 v 6

CHAPTER 5
FREEDOM ROAD

Walking in freedom proved to be more difficult than I had anticipated. I had spent so long on Tradition Road, being told what to do and even how to do it, that I found it rather overwhelming when faced with choices and decisions. Freedom Road was not long and straight and neatly fenced as my previous path had been – it wound in and out through the trees and there were many forks where a choice had to be made. Now and again we came to a huge roundabout that presented many choices and knowing which one to take was extremely difficult.

There were other difficulties too, other dangers I discovered. I was tramping around a great roundabout one day, trying to work out which road I should take, feeling confused and unhappy and cross, when I noticed some beautiful yellow flowers growing in the field beside the path. I ran quickly into the field to pick them, thinking that their beauty and bright colour might cheer me up and take my mind off the difficult decision I had to make.

I had only taken a few steps when I realised my mistake – what had looked like a beautiful green field was in fact a swamp and I was sinking fast. Too late I remembered what others had said about keeping on the path.

"Help! Somebody, help me!" I shouted. "I'm stuck in the swamp!"

For a moment I thought no one had heard me but then a pilgrim appeared at the edge of the field. I was relieved to see that he was tall and strong and also that he had a rope in his hand.

"Don't struggle!" he shouted. "Just try to catch the rope!"

It was hard not to struggle when the thick, slimy mud was sucking at my legs and pulling me deeper and deeper into the swamp but I sensed that I could trust this pilgrim. I did my best to keep still and concentrate on catching the rope, trying not to panic when the mud reached my waist. I missed the rope the first time but was able to catch it on the second throw.

When I had managed to tie it securely under my arms, the pilgrim began the slow process of pulling me in towards the path. As he did so, I noticed that some words had been woven into the fibres of the rope – 'help-in-time-of-need'. I began to wonder what sort of pilgrim carried a rope like that but suddenly I could feel solid ground under my feet again and I stumbled back on to the path, muddy and smelly but safe.

The pilgrim helped me to clean off the mud and gave me a drink from his water bottle before introducing himself.

"My name is Counsellor," he said. "How did you end up in the swamp?"

I noticed that he listened really carefully as I told him about my confusion and the beauty of the flowers that had distracted me from the path.

"You're not the first pilgrim to try to pick those flowers," he said. "That's one of the reasons I carry the help-in-time-of-need rope. The Master gave it to me as part of my equipment for my assignment in Kingdom Park."

I was pleased that he too knew the Master well and was intrigued to hear that he had been given a special assignment.

"Do you think the Master might have an assignment for me too?" I asked shyly. "I don't know much about Kingdom Park yet but maybe there is something I could do."

"Oh yes," he replied quickly, "everyone gets an assignment. I'm sure the Master will soon tell you about yours."

"Let me walk with you for a while," he continued. "I might be able to help you a little."

I was delighted that someone as strong and wise as Counsellor would offer to walk with me and accepted his offer immediately.

"The first thing I want to tell you about," he said, "is how to avoid getting stuck or distracted. As you have discovered, Freedom Road doesn't have any fences to keep you in."

"I was worried about that when I left Tradition Road," I told him. "I knew it would be harder to keep on the path but I didn't think I would be so easily distracted."

Counsellor guided me over to the edge of the path.

"Although there are no fences," he explained, "there are boundaries. You can't see them but they are marked here and there by boundary stones."

He pointed to a large stone at the edge of the path and I noticed that there were letters and numbers engraved in the stone.

"Oh I recognise that one," I said excitedly, tracing the writing with my finger. "E……. X………. 2…………. 0 – that's Exodus chapter 20. It's in the Book the Master gave me."

"Yes, we call that the Commandments chapter – the commandments are really important boundaries. The Book is full of boundaries – good principles that keep us on the path if we obey them."

Now that I knew what I was looking for, I ran to the next stone and called out the letters and numbers.

"P…….R…….O…….V…….. 3, 5 & 6 – that's Proverbs chapter 3 – what does the passage say?"

Counsellor laughed, "That would have been a good boundary for you a little while ago – you mightn't have ended up in the swamp if you had known about that one! It says to trust in the Lord with all your heart and not to lean on your own understanding. It tells you to acknowledge Him and He will direct your paths."

I laughed too and agreed, "Yes, instead of tramping round and round the roundabout trying to decide which way to go on my own, I should have asked the Master."

"Sometimes," I confided, "I find it hard to remember that He's there. His Presence isn't always real, if you know what I mean......."

Counsellor nodded his head as if to say that he too had sometimes felt like that, so I was encouraged to go on.

"I don't always hear His voice too clearly either," I confessed. "And sometimes I get His voice mixed up with all the other voices I hear. So I don't do anything because I'm scared that the voice I'm listening to is the enemy's voice."

I had never told any of the other pilgrims what I had confided in Counsellor and looked at him apprehensively but there was no look of judgement in his eyes, only understanding.

"Oh Child," he said and as he spoke my name, I realised that he sounded just like the Master, "everyone in Kingdom Park has the same difficulty at the beginning. It takes time to grow an awareness of His Presence and it takes time to know His voice. Look for the signs of His Presence like the peace-that-passes-understanding in your heart."

"Oh, I know what that feels like," I interrupted. "So that means He is close by?"

"Yes," Counsellor assured me, "that peace is a great indication of His Presence. And you know that lifting up of your heart when the pilgrims sing out their worship to the Father – that lets you know that the Master has drawn near."

Just then I felt that same little lift in my heart and sure enough, the Master was at my side. As His Peace enveloped me, I hardly noticed Counsellor turn around and move back down the path.

"I'll come if you need me," he called.

"I hope you won't need your rope next time!" I shouted back.

"I'm so glad I met Counsellor," I told the Master as we travelled on. "He was such a help to me. He told me that You gave him a special assignment – do You have one for me too?"

The Master smiled. "Just for the moment, Child," He said gently, "Your assignment is to get to know Me better. Later on there will be other work for you to do but your service needs to spring out of worship and love and relationship. Stay close to Me and listen carefully – you'll soon get to know me and to recognise My voice."

We walked together for some time along Freedom Road. His Presence was so real to me and His voice spoke so clearly and I longed that it would always be so. I knew, of course, that my humanity would often prevent me from experiencing His reality and His nearness. And although I so greatly enjoyed the company of other pilgrims and took much delight in joining their worship and studying the Book with them, I recognised that even their voices could sometimes drown out His voice.

As I contemplated these issues, we entered another roundabout and once again I followed its circular path, taking particular note of the signposts that led off it. I was careful this time to ask the Master to direct my path. The names intrigued me – Study Road, Silence and Solitude Path, Servanthood Highway and Leadership Lane. I would have been happy to travel along any of them except Silence and Solitude Path – I didn't really like the sound of that! I liked company and I liked to talk.

So the first time I walked around, I resisted the nudge I felt from the Master as we reached that particular path. The second time the nudge was so strong that I simply couldn't pretend I hadn't felt it and with some apprehension, I began to follow the Silence and Solitude Path.

My new path was such a contrast to Freedom Road – it was more like a country lane. It was narrow, presumably because not many pilgrims walked that way and it was tree-lined for sound proofing and privacy. Apart from a lone pilgrim in the distance, there was no one near me.

At first, the silence and the solitude were rather intimidating. In a strange way the silence seemed to shout loudly and the solitude seemed to crowd in on me. I couldn't understand what was happening so I asked the Master about it.

He gave a little laugh and said,
"The noise you hear that is so deafening is inside you! You didn't think you were so noisy, did you?"
I shook my head in disbelief. Surely the sounds I heard couldn't possibly inside my head?

"Your mind is a very busy place," the Master explained. "Your thoughts are constantly darting here and there, often unformed and at random, sometimes embarrassingly stupid, at other times unbelievably profound. The other voices and sounds in Kingdom Park keep your mind focussed but in the silence, you suddenly become more aware of your inner voice."

"But can I stop it?" I asked. "It's hard to concentrate on listening for Your voice or sensing Your Presence."
"Not really," the Master replied. "The Father gave you a busy mind – it would be no good at all if you didn't have any thoughts!"
"But you can learn to discipline your mind," He went on. "It's called 'taking thoughts captive.'"
"That sounds rather difficult," I protested.
The Master smiled,
"Well, you might like to start simply. When your mind is too busy in the silence, try just whispering My Name."

So I began by whispering the Master's Name – Jesus – and that reminded me that He was Lord of All so I whispered that too and my next thought was that He was also my Saviour and the Son of God and before I knew it, my mind was totally focussed on the Master and the busyness in my mind had calmed. As I continued to think of that Name-above-all-others, I realised that the Master seemed to be closer and His Presence more real than ever before.

Suddenly, into the silence, it seemed that the Master spoke, not really in words but in thoughts straight into my mind.

"When you go back to Freedom Road," I seemed to hear, "I want you to walk with that sad, lonely pilgrim you met recently and tell her I love her."

Then a verse from the Book came into my mind and I got the impression that I was to give that verse to her. I glanced at the Master and He nodded in confirmation.

"Yes, that often happens on Silence and Solitude Road," He said. "It's easier for me to communicate in the silence."

"I hadn't realised that this road would be so exciting," I exclaimed, "but I can also see that I can't follow it all the time – I need to constantly move from this road to other roads. It's no use keeping what I learn to myself – I have to share it with other pilgrims on other paths."

"That's right," the Master agreed. "I do call some pilgrims to long periods of their lives on Silence and Solitude Road but not everyone."

"Those who stay on this road must know You so well," I said and a surge of deep longing rose up in my heart.

"It's not in my plan for you, Child," the Master spoke gently. "Your assignment will require you to walk with other pilgrims and bring My words to them and you can't do that if you stay on this road all the time."

"My own assignment!" I breathed.

The Master smiled at my enthusiastic response and gestured to a place further up the road where a junction could be seen. Soon it would be time to join the busy, noisy, singing pilgrims on Freedom Road but I sensed that increasingly I would feel the gently nudge of the Master to follow the signpost to Silence and Solitude.

"I'll be back soon," I whispered as I ran on to Freedom Road, holding in my heart the words I had been given and the delight of His nearness and I wondered which road I would follow the next time I felt His gentle nudge.

THE LANGUAGE OF THE HEART

I come to God and He comes close to me,
I speak to God and He speaks back to me,
Not in the sounds and words that He has given to man
Not in the heavenly tongue the angels use to sing His praise,
But in the language of the heart.

I sense His presence and my heart is stilled
I feel His prompting and my heart is filled
With wonder that my God would speak to me
I hear His voice – the rhythm of my heart is stirred
I hear the language of the heart.

He speaks through eyes and ears that He has made
The earthly glories whose foundation He has laid
His Voice speaks loudly from the pages of His Word
My spirit stirs and rises to reach out to Him
Responding to the language of His heart.

*Let us come boldly
to the throne of grace.*

Hebrews ch 4 v 16

CHAPTER 6
COME

"The Father has sent an invitation to you," said the Master as He held out a beautifully decorated scroll. "Everyone who lives in Kingdom Park has received one."

My heart was filled with joy and excitement as I carefully broke the seal and opened the scroll. What would the invitation say – 'you are invited to a banquet……….. a wedding………. a private audience with the King……….?'

To my surprise it said none of those things – just one word filled the scroll, the word 'Come.' Although I was more than a little confused and didn't understand what the invitation meant, that single word contained such richness that it stirred up an amazing sense of warmth and welcome within my soul.

"What does it mean?" I asked the Master.

"This is an invitation that is open to you every day. The Father has a Table spread for all who live in Kingdom Park and He says 'Come.'"

Once again that word stirred something deep in my spirit.

"Lead me Lord," I whispered.

The Master walked before me along the path until we came to the Father's House and stood in front of its imposing entrance. I hesitated, unsure of what to do, afraid to cross the threshold.

"How do I get in?" I asked. "I have no key, I know no password and I'm afraid that His fire will consume me because of my unworthiness."

"Take a look at the doorposts," the Master directed and I stepped a little closer to see what He meant.

"Is that blood?" I asked. "Your blood?"

"Just walk right in," he urged me "My blood covers you. It's your key, your password to His Presence. You can be sure of His acceptance when My blood covers you."

And tears came to my eyes as I realised what it had cost the Master to purchase my acceptance. He had given His life so that I could cross this threshold without fear.

His smile acknowledged my tears and His hand under my elbow urged me on, so with great joy in my heart, I stepped into the Father's Presence. By this time many others had joined me, responding as I had to His call to 'Come'. I looked around, amazed at this great company of people who lived in Kingdom Park. As they crossed the threshold, I could see that there were many different responses to being in His Presence. Some raised their hands to heaven and burst into song, others knelt with their arms outstretched, shouting praise to the King, while others fell to their faces as though just being in His presence had drained all strength from their bodies. They lay there, motionless and not one of them spoke and not one of them sang – silent before the King.

And then I saw it – the table the Master had spoken of – the Father's Table. This magnificent Table stretched far into the distance and even from where I stood near the entrance, I could see that it was laden with food of every variety. Just then the Father's voice echoed down the hall – the same word I had read in the invitation scroll – 'Come'.

I wanted so much to respond, to draw near but no one else moved and so I held back, uncertain and afraid.

"All you need for life in Kingdom Park is on the Table," said the Master. "Take what you need."

I couldn't see the Table very well from where I stood so I moved a little closer, feeling conspicuous and rather embarrassed. The people all around me continued to pray and praise but still no one moved to partake from the Table.

The closer I got, the more clearly I could see the provision that had been made for me. The centrepiece was a huge golden chalice, filled to the brim and overflowing.

"That's Grace," said the Master, "the chalice is always full."

On either side of the chalice were sparkling cut-glass bowls, the word 'Mercy' engraved around each rim.

"You will need His Grace and His Mercy for your life in Kingdom Park," explained the Master, "Grace for those seasons when trials come and Mercy for the times you slip up and make mistakes."

Close to the bowls, I noticed a large china dish. Its pale cream colour, beautifully simple lines and understated pattern made it a worthy container for the provision it contained – the Peace-that-passes-understanding. I felt strangely drawn to this dish and knew in my heart that as soon as I had summoned the courage to approach the Table, it would be the first dish I would taste.

"You won't be able to take it all in just now," the Master remarked. "There are bowls of blessings, jugs of joy, fountains of forgiveness – always available and always poured out lavishly."

"Speaking of fountains," I asked, "what is that provision just a little further along? It looks a bit like a chocolate fountain……." And I gave a little giggle at the thought!

"Well," the Master smiled, "it works on the same principle. That's the Love fountain and just as the constantly flowing chocolate in a chocolate fountain coats whatever is held in it, so the Father's love flows eternally and covers over those who stand beneath it."

His words so delighted me that I could no longer resist. Somehow it ceased to matter that others were holding back like reluctant guests at a party and I ceased to care that I felt embarrassed or conspicuous.

"What does He require of me?" I asked.

"Simply to come and sit at His Table," was the reply. "Partake freely of His provision and commune with Him. He has promised that if you draw near to Him, He will draw near to you."

Filled with amazement that the Father, the God of the universe, should want to draw close to me and converse with me, I took my place at His Table. As I did so, I realised that many kingdom dwellers had been there all along. I just hadn't been able to see them.

What joy, what a deep sense of welcome and belonging I felt as I joined in the conversation at the Father's Table. I found it hard to believe that I was talking to the King and even harder to believe that He was talking to me. His voice was soft and gentle, heard more in my heart than in my ear and I understood instinctively that His was a voice that had to be obeyed.

All at once I knew without any doubt that no matter what I faced in Kingdom Park, when I obeyed His call to 'Come', I would find everything I needed for life. So I stretched out my hand towards the dish of peace……………….. mmm…………. How good it tasted…………… how glad I was that I had 'Come'.

FACE TO FACE

The God of Israel came down
He came in fire and cloud
The lightning flashed, the Voice of God
Roared out in thunders loud.

The God of Moses came and talked
As neighbours talk, in the Holy Place
God spoke to his friend in language plain
They met together face to face.

We know our God in a different way
Our spirit meets His face to face
No thunder, lightning, fire or cloud
Instead, a knowing which He grants by grace.

The solitary, silent hour
Is when we hear our Father's Voice
He speaks our names, pours out His love
We hear, we know – our hearts rejoice.

My grace is sufficient for you.

2 Corinthians ch 12 v 9

CHAPTER 7
THE GRACE HOUSE

We continued to journey together, the Master and I. I tried my best to follow where He led in Kingdom Park but it wasn't always easy to see the path ahead. I tried my best to listen to His voice when He spoke into my life but it wasn't always easy to understand what He was saying. I tried my best to use the weapons He had given me, the Word and Prayer but it wasn't always easy to remember.

So I suppose it was inevitable that I would make a big Mistake…….. an error of judgement……….. that I would sin. I was devastated to realise what I had done. All this time I had been living under the mistaken impression that once pilgrims entered Kingdom Park, they didn't make mistakes anymore, they didn't do wrong things, they didn't sin.

So I carried the guilt with me on my journey. At first I didn't notice it too much but the longer I carried it and the closer I walked to the Master, the heavier it became and the more awkward to carry. Eventually I got so weary of the burden that I stepped off the path, dug a hole in the soil and tried to bury it. But just when I had filled in the rest of the hole with some soil and stood up to walk away, I realised that the guilt was still there – it would not be buried. I cried out in frustration and the Master was instantly there at my side.

"What's the matter?" He asked and although I heard only love in His voice, such was my embarrassment and so big had the burden of guilt become, that I couldn't answer Him. I couldn't even look in His face.

"You've made a Mistake, you've sinned, haven't you?" He asked and I nodded miserably, waiting to hear words of condemnation and threats of punishment. That was how it had worked outside Kingdom Park – punishment and condemnation were the consequences of getting it wrong.

He seemed to know what I was thinking and simply said. "It's different in Kingdom Park. Come, let Me show you something."

I followed the Master, still too afraid to look in His face. But His words had brought a little hope to my heart and I wondered what it was He had to show me.

Soon we arrived at a large country house and as we made our way up the curve of the driveway, I noticed that the lights were lit in every room and it all looked warm and inviting.
"This is Grace House," He said. "This is where you bring your mistakes. Come in!"

So, still carrying my heavy, awkward burden of guilt for my Mistake, I followed Him into the House. He indicated that I should enter one of the doors and I was amazed to see that the entire room was being used to house a great display cabinet. I went closer to investigate and discovered that the cabinet held a single object – a huge, sparkling, brilliantly cut diamond. Dazzling rays of light shone from its surface.
"That looks amazing," I said with a question in my voice, "but what has it got to do with Mistakes?"

The Master smiled. "That's the Grace Gemstone," He replied. "Bring your guilt into the rays of its light."
I did as He instructed and watched in awe as the rays of Grace shone over my burden and completely covered it, causing it to shrink until there was no guilt remaining.

Now I was no longer afraid to look in His face for I knew I would see no condemnation there or hear no threat of punishment from His lips.

"My Grace is enough!" He said.

"Thank You, Master," I breathed. "I couldn't have carried the guilt of my Mistake for much longer. But tell me," I continued, "why is the Grace Gemstone shaped like a diamond?"

"That's because there are many facets to My Grace. Come and take a closer look."

As I drew nearer to the brightness of His Grace, I noticed that some words had been engraved into the faces.

"The Grace you received today is 'Grace-that-Covers-Sin'," the Master explained, "but if you walk all around the Grace Gemstone, you will see other aspects of My Grace."

I did as He suggested and found 'Grace-in-Trials' and 'Saving Grace'.

"Oh, I remember 'Saving Grace'," I said with delight. "that's what You gave me when I came to the Cross-shaped Gate into Kingdom Park. I've read about it in the Book too. I didn't deserve it but You gave it to me anyway."

"That's what My Grace is all about," He said with such pleasure in His voice that I could perceive something of the great joy He felt in sharing Grace with the pilgrims.

I looked again at the engraved words and, with some apprehension, asked Him about the 'Grace-in-Trials'.

"I hope I don't need that sort of Grace too often………." I said, looking at Him for some reassurance but none was forthcoming. He didn't even reply – just looked at me with a strange light in His eyes – and in that moment I sensed that I might indeed need this

Grace more often than I had hoped. The Master indicated that I should move on round the Gemstone and my amazement grew as I read all the words engraved on this huge, dazzling stone. I saw 'Grace-in-Persecution', 'Grace-in-Sorrow', 'Grace-in-Sickness', 'Grace-in-Broken-Relationships', 'Grace-in-Disappointment' and 'Grace-in-Impossible-Places'. As I continued to explore the riches of His Grace, I realised that there was no circumstance in life that His Grace could not cover.

"My Grace is enough," He whispered again. "It is all you require. Come as often as you need to the Grace House. My Grace is lavish – the Father delights to pour it out without measure. My Grace is never-failing. Don't ever be afraid that it will run out."

"There will always be Grace," He added with a smile as we left Grace House and resumed our journey through Kingdom Park, "Amazing Grace!"

ENTER THE SILENCE

Enter the silence –
That's where you'll find Me
When times are hard
And words don't easily express
The pain and hurt inside.

Whisper your cry to Me
'Here I am, I need You'
Then climb on to My lap
Rest your aching head
And wait for peace.

Hold to My promise
That as you lie, child-like,
Within the circle of My arms
I will send My peace
To fill your heart.

I have all you need
And I'll envelop you
With strength and peace and grace.
My loving hand will wipe away
The tears of sadness running down your face.

Hide me in the shadow of Your wings.

Psalm 17 v 8

CHAPTER 8
IN THE SHADOW

I walked into the shadow and immediately it was dark and cold. I was afraid to go on because I could not longer see the path ahead. No matter how hard I tried to peer into the darkness, I could see no end to the shadow. I longed to go back, to step into the sunshine but knew that to be impossible. So, feeling frightened and alone, I sat down at the edge of the greyness and cried bitter tears of helplessness and frustration.

It was then the Master spoke to my heart and made me aware of His Presence. "How did I come to this terrible place?" I cried out to Him in despair. "Why is this shadow hanging over me? Did I do something wrong? Is this shadow my punishment?"

"My dear child", he replied, "I drew you here."

I looked at him in astonishment. Why would the Master want to bring me to this darkness, to this place, where I was afraid to take another step in case I stumbled and fell, to this place where the sun of His love no longer shone? Oh, I knew in my heart that His love was still shining as brightly as ever beyond the shadow but I could no longer feel its warmth on my face, invigorating me and making me smile with delight. There could be no other explanation save that I had displeased Him.

He knew what I was thinking and hastened to reassure me.

"This is not a punishment, child," He said softly, "you have done nothing wrong. I drew you here simply because it is part of My plan for you. You need to know Me in the shadow, in the dark and lonely place."

"This is actually the shadow of My wings. At the moment you can only sense the greyness and the coldness but this is really a most secure place to be. My wings of care and protection are all around you. There may be darkness but there should be no fear, for no one can harm you when you are enclosed in My wings."

I was somewhat comforted by His words but the awful blackness continued to bother me.

"Master," I cried. "I can see no light at all, not even far away in the distance. Is there no end to the shadow? Will it always be like this?"

"I know it seems that the shadow lasts forever but trust Me child, one day I will lift My wings and the sun will once more come streaming in, all around you. Until that day, be patient and sing for Me."

I was sure I hadn't heard Him correctly.

"Did you say 'sing'? How could I possibly sing? There is nothing to sing about in this place of shadows. I might just manage to survive it now that I know about Your wings but please don't ask me to sing."

"Come now," His voice was warm with encouragement, "just try. Sing for Me."

"But what shall I sing?" I asked.

"Just sing what is in your heart," was His reply.

The Master took me by the hand and raised me to my feet, and as He held my hand to reassure me of His Presence, I began to sing. At first I sang of darkness and my despair and the song of my heart was a plaintive melody in a minor key. It seemed to be a never-ending song whose notes hung eerily in the shadows.

Then, very slowly, I began to recognise a change – a gentle modulation to a major key as my heart's song ceased to speak of my loneliness and fear but sang instead of the closeness of the Master and the encompassing protection of His wings.

And soon my voice rang out strong and true and the melody of my heart soared and even in the darkness, there was joy. And standing there, I suddenly realised that it didn't matter how long He kept me in the shadow or how often I would find myself returning to its greyness, He would be there and the song would always be in my heart. I had learnt to sing in the shadow of His wing.

HIS SONG, MY SONG

He gave to me a song,
And all the notes were given,
And all the harmonies I'd need
To sing my song from Heaven.

He said, "Come, sing your song,
When joy and peace are all you see,
But also sing when life is rough –
It still sounds sweet in a minor key."

I raised my voice and sang His song
And knew within, He sang with me,
My heart rejoiced to understand
I'd sing this song for eternity.

He is like a tree
  planted by streams of water.

Psalm 1 v 3

CHAPTER 9
LIKE A TREE

"If you are ever trying to think of a picture for a church," the Master remarked one day, "this is as good as it gets."

He had stopped beside a huge tree and indicated that we should sit down to rest for a while in its shade.

I knew that the Book used pictures to describe the Church – I had read of the 'body' and the 'building' and remembered that the Psalmist David had likened a Godly man to a tree planted by the riverside but I had never thought of the local church, the group of pilgrims with whom I met each week, in that way.

As I began to consider the imagery, of course, it made perfect sense.

"Well," I began to think out loud, "a tree has one central trunk."

We were leaning against the trunk of the great tree and I could sense its strength and stability.

"I suppose that speaks of leadership. When this tree was a young sapling, its trunk was thin and easily bent but each year a new ring of wood was added and now it is strong enough to carry the weight of all the branches and leaves it supports."

The Master smiled. "That's right," He said, "if the trunk isn't strong enough, the weight of the branches could pull it over and cause it to snap. If church leaders aren't mature and strong, they too can be pulled down and broken."

I thought with sadness of some of the churches in Kingdom Park where that had happened, leaving behind a damaged, wounded people. My thoughts were interrupted by some strange sounds above my head.

"Now that is really weird," I exclaimed, "it sounds as though the branches are talking to each other."

I looked at the Master for some clarification but He just motioned me to listen. Soon I realised that what I was hearing was not just a discussion but an argument.

"I'm telling you, our job is to provide a place for the birds to build nests," said one branch and when I looked up carefully, I could see a beautifully crafted nest that had been built where the branch forked into two.

"You're so wrong," protested another branch, "our main assignment in Kingdom Park is to provide shade," and he gently dipped his leaves up and down to fan the animals resting below.

"You two think you know it all," shouted a branch much higher up the tree, "and you know nothing! If you had any sense you would understand that our sole purpose is to provide food for the insects."

As He waved his branch in triumph, I could see that his leaves were laced with tiny holes where hungry caterpillars had chewed.

"No, no," called another branch that had grown out straight from the trunk, "we're here for the children – they tie ropes to me for swings and climb on me and sometimes even build a tree house."

And so the argument continued – "We're landmarks………."
"No, we're meeting places…………….."
" I'm convinced we're meant to give fruit for jam…………………"
" We sacrifice our wood as firewood to keep the pilgrims warm……………………."
"That's a waste of resources – our wood should be used for making things that will last – stylish furniture and mighty

ships…………."

Each branch was convinced that his purpose was the sole purpose for the tree.

"Church members do that too, don't they?" I asked the Master. "They argue a lot about the Father's plan for them. So who's right?"

The Master took a moment to answer and I sensed that the argument distressed Him.

"In one way they're all right," He replied at last, "and in another way, they're all wrong! The Father planted them in Kingdom Park for His Glory – to live and grow and be. Many pilgrims don't realise the importance of 'being' but the Father is actually more concerned with your 'being' that with your 'doing' – being in relationship with Him, being in His Presence, being His child……………… and the churches can also bring Him Glory through worship and by bearing fruit."

"That is the underlying purpose of any church and indeed of any individual pilgrim," He continued, "but He does also expect His churches to respond to the needs around them so it is right for them to rescue those outside the gate, as Rescuer did for you and to provide support for the journey through Kingdom Park."

I smiled as I remembered Rescuer's efforts to encourage me through the gate and Counsellor's help when I got stuck in the swamp. How grateful I was for what they had done.

"Unfortunately," the Master went on, "it's easy for pilgrims to simply respond to need and forget about the desire of the Father that their lives and their church should first of all bring Glory to Him."

While He talked, I had noticed a branch whose leaves had faded and were dry and brittle. Some had already fallen to the ground and been trampled underfoot.

"What has happened to that branch?" I asked and the Master

looked to where I was pointing.

"One thing you must learn about a tree," He told me, "is that the sap has to be able to flow freely through it for life to be sustained. For some reason the sap in this branch has ceased to flow and it is slowly dying."

His face softened as He continued.

"The sap in My church is the Great Spirit. When He is allowed to flow freely and unhindered through My people, My church thrives and grows. New pilgrims enter Kingdom Park and the fruit of the Spirit is soon evident in their lives. Suffering, broken pilgrims are supported and comforted. Words given by My Spirit bring strength and encouragement. Buds break forth into blossom and bear fruit. I love watching My church, My bride when she is working well."

"So is there any hope for the dying branch?" I asked somewhat fearfully.

"Just watch," He instructed.

He reached out His hand and ran it along the branch, stripping away the rest of the dead leaves. Then he very carefully examined the branch and to my horror, he suddenly snapped off part of it!

"Oh," I exclaimed, "what did you do that for?"

"The branch needs to be pruned," He replied. "Come closer and look."

As I moved closer, I noticed that the Master had taken hold of the jagged edge where the branch had broken off and was covering it with His special balm for wounds.

"The branch will heal," He assured me. "Now tell me, what do you see just there?"

He pointed to a place close to where He had pruned and when I looked closely, I could just make out a tiny bulge on the branch and in the centre of the bulge, a tiny spot of green.

"It's a little green shoot!" I exclaimed with great joy. "It's a sign of new life. The branch isn't completely dead!"

"When I prune," the Master said, "My intention isn't to damage or destroy but to enable the branch to bear more fruit or to reshape the tree. There are many reasons why the sap doesn't flow – sinful lives, wrong attitudes, pride, apathy, fear, unforgiveness, disunity, bitterness. These have to be dealt with in individual lives and also in churches."

I was almost afraid to ask the next question, "What if they are not dealt with?"

His face darkened as He drew my attention to a tree stump nearby.

"The Father may eventually take away all the branches and some of the trunk," He said sadly.

My stomach lurched and my heart began to pound.

"How awful," I whispered tearfully. "Does the Father give them any warning?"

"The Father is always gracious and compassionate, My child," He reassured me. "He will call His people to repentance time and time again. He has a heart full of mercy and will patiently speak to His people until they listen and obey but He will not chide forever."

I was careful to store His words up in my heart. At some time in the future, I might need to be reminded of this moment. I might need these words of His to warn a pilgrim group in some corner of Kingdom Park of the terrible consequences of refusing to heed the Father's call. And I looked deep into my own heart to search out my attitudes and motives. Oh that my sole desire might be to bring Him Glory.

THE GENTLE DOVE

John ch 1 v 32 I saw the Spirit come down from heaven as a dove and remain on Him.

The Spirit rests so lightly on my life.
Though conscious of His Presence day by day,
I know that when I speak an angry word,
The Spirit spreads His wings and flies away.

The Spirit rests so lightly on my life,
Teaching, guiding, filling every day.
But if I don't forgive the least offence,
The Gentle Dove takes flight and will not stay.

The Spirit rests so lightly on my life.
The Comforter and Friend can't stay
When bitterness takes root inside my heart -
He quickly spreads His wings and flies away.

Oh Gentle Dove, remain upon my life.
Indwell me as I worship, serve and pray
And may I be surrendered to Your will.
Oh do not spread Your wings and fly away.

CHAPTER 10
SPIRIT RESERVOIR

I had noticed the two cottages in the distance as we continued our journey through Kingdom Park. There seemed to be a lot of activity around both houses and I began to wonder what was happening. As we drew nearer, I could see that a man was sitting outside the first cottage and seemed to be encouraging the pilgrims who were passing by to visit his home.

The cottages were close together, identical in size and shape and were even painted in the same colours. The only difference I could see was that the man outside the second cottage kept popping in and out of his house. He didn't seem to be calling out to the passing pilgrims but many of them called him over to them and seemed to be questioning him about his house.

By this time we had arrived at the first cottage and the Master told me to take a seat on a bench by the side of the road.

"Now watch and listen," He instructed.

I was happy to do so as I was not only extremely curious but also very tired.

"Come and see," the man began to call to those who were walking past. "You won't have seen anything like this before," he continued and one or two pilgrims stopped to listen to him.

"The water tank takes up the entire roof space," I heard him shout excitedly. "I can give you the exact dimensions."

He beckoned them over and opened the book in his hand.

"See, that's the width and length and that's the height – as high as possible in the roof space. And just look at the volume of water it holds," he continued with great enthusiasm, pointing to the statistics in the book.

"Have you ever seen anything like that?" he enquired. "Would you like to come and see how it all works?"

The pilgrims seemed to be rather impressed by what they had been told and followed the man into his cottage. I was consumed with curiosity so, after looking to the Master for approval, I followed the pilgrims into the house.

The man opened a trapdoor into the roof space and encouraged us all to climb a narrow ladder to see the water tank. It was an amazing sight – a huge tank, made of strong, thick glass, taking up the entire roof space and filled to the brim with the cleanest water I had ever seen.

I put out my hand to touch the glass but was quickly rebuked by the owner.

"Oh no, you mustn't touch," he said. "I don't want to get finger prints on the tank. Now just look at the complex system of pipes – there is a pipe that lets the water flow to every room in the house. Come down now and I'll show you."

He led us through all the rooms and showed how in some rooms, the pipes led to radiators for heating, while in others, they led to baths and showers, hand basins and sinks.

"The water is the purest in Kingdom Park, the pipes will never rust or wear out and the taps are made of gold," he pointed out proudly. "Isn't it all amazing?"

One of the pilgrims seemed to know a lot about plumbing and he asked a few technical questions to which the man gave long, detailed answers. I understood neither the questions nor the answers!

By this time we had come back to the front door, just as another pilgrim arrived, red-faced and panting. He must have been running on the path for a long time.

"Please Sir," he gasped, "could I have a drink of water? I'm so thirsty."

I was astonished to hear the reply.

"Oh no, I'm afraid not," the man told him, his face stern and forbidding. "I don't ever use any of it. I have to make sure it all stays in my tank. But do come in – I can show you how it all works."

The pilgrim just looked at him wearily and turned away from the door. His shoulders drooped and he seemed to be dragging one foot after the other. I felt so sorry for him.

"Why won't he give him some water?" I asked the Master, angry and distressed at the man's lack of concern.

"Keep watching," the Master encouraged me, putting His hand on my arm to comfort me.

As the pilgrim approached the other cottage, I was so afraid that the owner would also refuse to share his water. I didn't think the pilgrim would be able to go much further.

I heard him ask for a drink as before, though his voice was so weak I could hardly make out the words. To my relief, the response was quite different this time. The cottage owner rushed inside and came out, not just with a drink of water but with a huge jug of water as well.

"Drink your fill," I heard him say, "there is plenty more in the tank."

I turned to the Master for some explanation of what I had seen but He simply indicated that I should follow Him.

"I want to show you Spirit Reservoir," He said.

We walked for miles, following the path of the pipes that led to the two cottages. As we climbed into the mountains, the diameter of the pipes got larger and larger and other pipes branched off them, presumably to feed the water to other parts of Kingdom Park. It was so quiet this high in the mountains that I could hear the gushing of the water through the pipes.

We came eventually to a great valley in the mountains, across which an enormous dam had been built.

"This is Spirit Reservoir," the Master said, as I gazed in wonder at the huge lake that had been created by the dam. It stretched far into the distance, so far that I couldn't even be sure that it ever ended.

As I tried to drink in the beauty of the vast, mountain-ringed lake, the Master began to speak.

"Everyone who lives in Kingdom Park has access to the water in Spirit Reservoir. Each pilgrim who builds his home in the Park has a tank that fills his roof space."

"Everyone?" I interrupted, "Even me?"

"Even you," the Master smiled. " You can read about it in the Book – it's called a deposit."

"The water of the Spirit," He continued, "flows freely through the huge pipes from the reservoir to the homes and keeps the tanks filled up."

"So why was the man in the first cottage not able to give the thirsty pilgrim a drink?" I asked.

"It's a very simple reason," the Master replied. "He had never turned on the taps."

"Oh," I exclaimed, "that explains something else that puzzled me greatly about the first owner. He had a great tank of clean, clear water but the floors in his house were really dirty, the dishes in the sink had never been washed and the man himself............ well, you know..........."

I held my nose between my finger and thumb and the Master nodded His understanding.

"It's a shame, isn't it?" He said. "But many pilgrims in Kingdom Park do the same. The water of the Spirit is given for cleansing and drinking and refreshing but so many are content to have the tank and the sturdy pipes and the golden taps but never use the water."

"But he knew so much about how it all worked," I said sadly.

"Yes," the Master agreed, "many have studied the Great Spirit for years and can discuss at great length what the Book has to say about Him but they never turn on the tap and allow His divine water to flow over them and make them clean."

"But why do they do that?" I asked in bewilderment.

The Master led me down the valley again as He began to explain.

"Well, some pilgrims really do believe that they're not supposed to turn on the taps, that it's enough to know about the tank and the reservoir and how it works, others are just simply afraid of what might happen if they turn the taps on – they know that the water of the Spirit is living water but they have become accustomed to their homes and their lives and don't want anything to change. And some pilgrims realise that if the taps are turned on, they will have to clean their house and that seems like too much hard work."

I began to feel quite embarrassed as the Master talked – I could identify with some of those pilgrims. I was too ashamed to tell the Master that my house had dirty floors, that I too had been afraid to turn on the taps.

For a long time, we walked in silence. In my heart a great battle raged – I knew what I should do but there was a fearful part of me, deep inside, that held me back. I knew I should talk to the Master about how I felt but I was so ashamed I couldn't even raise my eyes to look at His face.

We made our way down between the two cottages and to my surprise, the weary pilgrim was still outside the second one. The glass and the jug were both empty and the pilgrim was wet from head to foot! His eyes were dancing and his smile stretched from ear to ear.

My battle forgotten for a moment, I rushed over to question him.

"What happened? Why are you so wet and happy?"

"It's the water," he laughed, "When I drank it my weariness vanished and then the owner suggested that a shower might refresh me. I was so energized by the water that I rushed straight into the bathroom and never even stopped to remove my clothes! I turned the shower on as far as it would go – it was wonderful!"

He started to laugh and his laughter was so infectious that I couldn't help myself joining in.

"It's hard to describe," he went on when he had recovered enough to speak, "but I feel as though I am properly clean – clean in a way I have never been before. My skin is tingling and even the clothes I'm wearing feel different – as though they fit me better now………"

His voice tailed off and he shook his head as though lost for words.

"It's just hard to describe," he repeated as he began to walk on down the path, now and then giving a little jump and a skip as he went.

I too set off down the path, running as fast as I could go.

"Where are you going?" the Master called after me.

"Home – to turn on the taps!" I shouted, laughing as I ran. And in the distance, I could hear the Master's voice as His laughter mingled with mine.

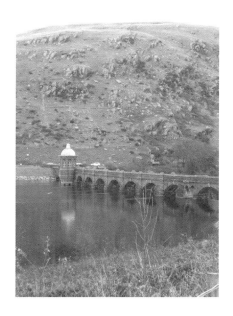

Streams of living water
will flow from within him.
John ch 7 v 38

COME, SWEET SPIRIT, COME

Come, Sweet Spirit, come.

Father God, I've heard the whisper of His breath
And felt the gentle rustling of His breeze,
But now my heart cries out to You O Lord,
For the Spirit's mighty wind to drive me to my knees.

Father God, there have been times when deep inside
I've known a tiny spark of Spirit fire,
Sweet Spirit, come and fan that feeble flame
Till Jesus, only Jesus, becomes my one desire.

Father God, I've seen the trickle of His joy
Flow through my soul in sweet refreshing song,
Spirit of God, my heart is waiting for the floods -
For springs of joy, for rivers of delight I long.

Come, Sweet Spirit, come.

Come as a mighty rushing wind,
Blow away the chaff of worthless things inside;
Come as a cleansing flame of fire,
Burn up the dross of selfishness and pride.

Then, as a clean and empty vessel,
I shall wait with longing in my soul,
For the flood tide of the Spirit's joy and power
Into my heart in mighty waves to roll.

Come, Sweet Spirit, come.

MY HEART YEARNS

A great yearning
    A longing
        An ache.

For Your Glory
    For Your Presence
        For You.

Come, visit us
    Don't walk away
        Stay here.

Rend the Heavens
    Send Your Spirit
        Come down.

Just invite Me
    Just ask Me
        I will come.

"He acted as if He were going further but they urged Him strongly: Stay with us, for it is nearly evening."
Luke ch 24 v 28

I want to come more than you want Me to come.

I have My fingers poised on the Heavens,
My Spirit knows the same yearning
the same longing, the same ache.

My Glory waits at the door.
My Presence is only lightly veiled.
    I will come.

When your yearning meets Mine
When your longing is enveloped in Mine
When your heart feels the ache of My heart.
    I will come.

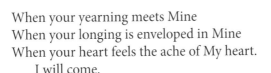

You will fill me with joy in Your Presence.

Psalm 16 v 11

CHAPTER 11
LEAN ON ME

Since I had discovered the secret of letting the Master take the lead in our journey together, I was enjoying the walk so much more. There were still hills to climb, rocky places to cross and fast-flowing rivers to wade through but somehow when He showed me where to place my feet, I didn't stumble or fall quite as often as I had previously.

So we walked the path together.

"Isn't this just wonderful?" I said to my Companion. "I can't imagine a better way to live."

The Master smiled and then just as He began to reply to me, a noisy group of fellow pilgrims passed us and I couldn't hear what He said. They were singing and shouting praise to the Father and my heart responded to their joy and my lips joined in their praise. We walked together for many miles and I knew that our praise must have pleased the Father's heart but now and again, I felt a strange tug deep in my spirit and I wondered what it was the Master had wanted to say to me.

Soon the pilgrims ran on ahead of me. They were younger and fitter and able to climb the hills with greater ease so I slowed my pace and the Master matched His step to mine as we continued our journey.

"I do love walking like this, knowing that You're close beside me," I whispered as I gazed up into the Master's face. I saw His lips move but once again His words were drowned out, this time by loud cries from the side of the road.

I turned to see who was in such distress and was dismayed to find a large group of pilgrims lying crying in the dust, reaching out their hands to me. As I knelt by the first pilgrim and saw his deep wounds, I realised that the Master was also at his side gathering him in His arms and healing his wounds. For the rest of the day we worked side by side, the Master and I, until every poor, hurting pilgrim had felt the Master's touch.

By this time it was evening and my strength had gone.

"I can't go on, Lord," I cried, "I'm exhausted…… I can't take another step. And I'm so frustrated……. Twice You have spoken to me today and I didn't hear what You said."

I sat down at the edge of the road and wept bitterly.

"Lord, this road is so hard. It's too noisy to hear You. It's too busy…. There are too many people who need help."

Then over my weeping I heard Him speak my name.

"Come," He said, "take My hand. I'll show you where to go for renewed strength and vigour."

I reached out and as His hand touched mine, I was amazed to find that energy flowed, enough to enable me to follow Him along the path again.

"What I want to reveal to you is just around the corner. We'll soon be there."

I made my way along slowly, still quite drained from serving Him that day but curious to see what He had in store for me. Just beyond the corner, we came to a small structure by the side of the road, rather like a bower. Beautiful sweetly-scented flowers grew all over the bower but I couldn't see any door or entrance. I looked at the Master with a question in my eyes.

"Oh, there is a door," He assured me with a smile, "but many people walk by and miss it."

I went in a little further and there on my left was a tiny door. Written on it were the words, "The Listening Place".

I opened the door and went inside with great excitement in my heart.

"I'm sure this will be such a beautiful place," I thought, expecting to see bright colours, fine furniture and possibly even the newest technology to help me listen.

"Oh…" I gasped in disappointment as I looked around what must have been the plainest room I had ever seen. There were no windows, only plain, white walls and ceiling and a simple wooden floor. There was only one piece of furniture – a single white settee on which were embroidered the words, "His Presence".

"Come and sit," He invited and I obeyed His voice, amazed to discover as I did so, that in some strange way, the settee seemed to envelop me! I was more aware of His Presence than I had ever been before – it seemed to flood me with joy, fill up my emptiness and calm my anxiety. The Master was beside me but also all around me and in me, above me and beneath me.

Any sense of disappointment fled as I heard Him say,

"The room is plain because My Presence is all you need. It has no decorations so that there will be nothing to distract you from Me. There are no windows so you won't be aware of anything or anyone else, only of Me."

"Oh can I just stay here forever?" I breathed.

He laughed aloud at my foolishness.

"No Child, this is where you receive strength for the ministry I've given to you – energy and enthusiasm to sing with the praising pilgrims and deep compassion for the wounded ones. You can't stay here because you and I have work to do together. But come here often. You'll always find My Presence in the Listening Place."

And then I felt His arms pull me closer to Him. I pulled back and straightened up again.

"What's wrong, Child?" He enquired.

"I'm afraid......... such intimacy scares me a little........... being so close feels like being overwhelmed."

I began to weep softly. There was such an ache in my heart to be that close and I couldn't even fully understand what was holding me back.

"I know your heart, little one," He whispered so tenderly, "but you don't ever have to be afraid of Me or of My Presence. Those who love Me learn to lean on Me, learn to trust themselves to My embrace."

And so, little by little, I yielded to His touch and His arm pulled me closer and closer until my head rested on His heart. And all was still and quiet and no one sang and no one cried and His lips were so close to my ear that I could hear even the softest whisper.

It seemed that time stood still as I lay in His Presence and listened to His voice and He told me all that I needed to hear. He spoke of His unfailing love for me, of His desire to fill me with His Spirit, of the grace that would always be at my disposal and shared with me the secret of the power in His Name. In the stillness, as I pressed closer to Him, I realised that I could hear His heart beat – the heart beat of God Himself! And my own heart leaped within me in response.

"Is this what Heaven will be like?" I asked.

The Master laughed again.

"No," He whispered, "it will be even better. At the moment I have to veil your eyes when you enter My Presence, lest My holiness consumes you but in Heaven, there'll be no veil. You'll see me face to face."

So I rested in the Listening Place, leaning on the Master with my head on His heart, listening to His voice, my heart beating to the rhythm of His heart. And I felt once more the ache of longing in my soul for what one day would be a glorious reality.

RETREAT PRAYER

So here I am, Lord
I've entered the silence
Stilled and quietened my heart
Obeyed Your call to come apart.

I'll stay here, Lord,
Until I've met with You
I really need to hear Your voice
Speak but one word and I'll rejoice.

I've known before, Lord,
The wonder of Your coming
Your glorious presence filling me
Giving me ears to hear and eyes to see.

So come again, dear Lord,
Speak in a still, small voice
Whisper your love, Your peace, your grace
Meet with me in this trysting place.

SILENT MOMENTS

It took a while to fix my mind on You
To push the busyness of life aside
To calm the anxious, darting thoughts
To sit with You and just abide.

I wonder, Lord, how many times
You sit and wait and watch for me
But I rush past You as You wait
I've things to do and friends to see.

The silent moments spent with You
Are sweet and rich as I draw near
Released from tyranny of words
I listen and Your voice I hear.

Remind me, Lord, to sit with You
To carve out time from busy days
To let Your voice flow through my mind
To know Your thoughts, find out Your ways.

O may I yearn to be with You
To sense Your Presence, know You're near
Feel Your touch deep in my heart
Listen for Your whisper in my ear.

Forgive and you will be forgiven.

Luke ch 6 v 37

CHAPTER 12
LET GO

"That's it! I've had enough! How dare they? How could they say such things? How could they treat me like that?"

My angry thoughts tumbled one over the other as I slowed my pace and fell behind the group of pilgrims who had been my companions. I could feel my whole body tensing as I thought over the events of the previous few days. My stomach turned over and for a moment I thought I was going to be sick by the side of the road. A darting pain heralded the beginning of a headache and a huge lump gathered in my throat. I fought back the tears and sought desperately for somewhere to hide.

Life in Kingdom Park had been so good until a few days before. I had been walking with the same group of pilgrims for a long time, since the day I had discovered the joys of Freedom road. Joining with them in worship was one of my greatest delights and listening to them pray encouraged me to lift up my voice before the Father's throne too. Many of them walked close to the Master and seemed to understand the mysteries of the Book really well so I had learnt a great deal from them about following in His footsteps. I made friends in the group and eventually trusted them enough to share my heart with them. They welcomed my confidences, discussed my aspirations and invited me to share my dreams.

I was overjoyed to have found a group of pilgrims who understood me so well and accepted me so warmly. I felt safe and comfortable in their company – so much so that as we walked together one day, I shared with them my Secret.

I had carried the Secret for many years. I had brought it with me when I entered Kingdom Park, brought it with me from my old life. The Secret had damaged me and caused me much distress. I had never told the Secret to anyone before – I had been too ashamed, I had felt too guilty.

The response of the little group was immediate.

"Your secret is safe with us," they cried. "Don't worry. It will be alright – we'll help you."

I was greatly comforted by their words and relieved to have finally given voice to the Secret. Somehow sharing it had made its burden less. I rejoiced and gave thanks to the Father for helping me to find such a wonderful group of pilgrims to accompany me on my journey.

And then, a few days later – disaster struck!

I was walking close enough to one of the group to be able to overhear his conversation and was appalled by what I heard. He was telling another pilgrim the Secret! My mouth fell open and my heart began racing. I nearly cried out but stifled the sound and moved a little closer so that I could hear more clearly.

"What do you think of that?" I heard him say. "Isn't it dreadful! She should be ashamed of herself."

His companion agreed and continued in pious tones,

"You know, the Book says we should be holy and separate. I don't think you should allow her to walk with you any more."

"Oh I had wondered about that myself," my friend responded. "I'd better talk to the others in the group and see what they think."

With that, he moved away and I hurriedly crossed to the other side of the road where I was hidden from sight by a group of pilgrims who were passing by. I thought my heart would break. How could he betray me? How could he so easily give away the Secret

I had hidden so carefully for many years? Despite my distress, I nursed a little hope that perhaps he was the only one in the group to feel like that but it became apparent over the next few days that it was not to be.

I continued to walk with them, trying to hide my heartache but then, in the most humiliating experience of my life, they had revealed the Secret to the whole group. One by one they flung their accusations in my face and their hard words shocked me to the core. I looked for some support from others in the group but saw only judgement and condemnation in their eyes. That was it – I had had enough! The betrayal was too much to bear.

As I looked around frantically for somewhere to hide, I realised that I had stopped very close to the little hidden door of the Listening Place. Quickly I ran inside and the floodgates opened as I threw myself on to the white settee and His Presence once more enveloped me.

I cried out to the Master in my pain and distress.

"How could they betray me like that? I didn't think that pilgrims who live in Kingdom Park could behave so cruelly!"

The more I thought of what they had done, the more the pain increased. Each harsh word they had said reverberated in my memory and their judgemental frowns danced like flashbacks before my eyes.

"I hate them!" I shouted. "I never want to see them again! I'll never speak to them as long as I live!"

The Master had said nothing during my torrent of anger and grief but His Presence was very real and soon the sobs began to subside and I felt His hand wipe away the last of the tears. Then, in the stillness, I heard His whisper,

"You must forgive."

I couldn't believe what I had heard. Forgive? Not a chance! I jumped up and stormed out through the door, slamming it behind me in rage.

"Why should I forgive them?" I cried. "They have ruined my life!"

So I closed my ears to His whisper and set off once more along the path. I held to my resolution and refused to walk with my former companions. They came to find me and made attempts to apologise but I refused to hear their words. They asked for my forgiveness but I refused to speak to them. After a while they stopped trying to talk to me and I was rather relieved when we came to a fork in the road and I was able to take a different path to theirs.

Eventually I found another group to walk with and I pushed the issue of my betrayal and the Master's whisper to the back of my mind. The Master continued to accompany me and guide me but now and again I would see a sad look in His eyes and when that happened, a faint whisper could be heard .... "You must forgive........."

Then one day I rounded a corner and was startled to find my way blocked. A thick hedge of brambles and thorns had grown right across the path. I looked all around for another road but there was no way past. I was stuck. I tried to go back the way I had come but a bramble hedge had grown up behind me. In Kingdom Park, there was no going back, only forward.

I sat down at the foot of the hedge and called out to the Master. He came to sit with me and the sadness was in His eyes again.

"I'm stuck," I cried. "I want to go on, I want to serve You – You know I do! I don't understand what has happened!"

The Master looked at me and then looked at the hedge – thick and high and impassable.

"That hedge," He said sadly, "is the hedge of Unforgiveness. Each time you spoke an angry word against your fellow pilgrims, another thorn bush grew. Each time you allowed bitter thoughts to stay in your mind, the hedge grew taller. Each time you were challenged to forgive and refused, the brambles entwined the branches and the hedge got thicker."

"In Kingdom Park," He went on, "forgiveness isn't a choice. It's a command from the Father Himself. You heard My words many times – 'you must forgive' – but you closed your ears and you closed your heart. So now I can't use you to work in the Kingdom – the Unforgiveness Hedge has blocked your path."

I gazed at the hedge and I looked at the Master in dismay.
"My thoughts and attitudes built this hedge?" I asked, reluctant to believe what He was telling me.
"And You can't use me if I won't forgive?"
The Master nodded but said nothing.
"But they hurt me so much," I moaned, insistent that He would understand my position. "What they did was wrong, what they said was untrue!"

The Master nodded but again said nothing. I searched my heart in the stillness ……………… could I bring myself to forgive?
"I don't think I can," I said finally. "I don't think I can forgive them. I have a right to be angry."

So together we waited beside the hedge. There was no way forward and there was no way back. After a long time, I glanced at the Master and as I did so, a faint memory came back to me – a memory of the day I had stood at His cross with my huge knapsack of sin weighing me down. The Master's eyes met mine – He was remembering too – and I lowered my gaze in shame.
"You forgave me," I murmured, "forgave everything."

The memory of His love, His forgiveness reached into my bitterness and the hard places in my heart began to melt.

"You must forgive," He said softly, "as I forgave you. You must let go of what you are holding against them. Let go, Child, don't keep building the hedge."

The tears came then – no longer tears of resentment for my betrayal but tears of sorrow and repentance for my bitter, unforgiving spirit.

"Show me what to do," I cried. "Show me how to forgive."

"Speak out your forgiveness," the Master said, "and then walk in it. I'll strengthen you and uphold you."

So, rather hesitantly at first, I spoke out my forgiveness, naming those who had wronged me and releasing them from the bondage of my bitterness. And as I named each person, I watched in amazement as the brambles withered and the thorns died. I named the last person and rushed over to the hedge to make my way through but found that although the hedge was thinner and smaller, it still blocked my path.

"What's the matter now?" I asked in dismay. "There isn't anyone else to forgive."

The Master smiled, "What about yourself? Many pilgrims forget to forgive themselves!"

So once more I spoke out my forgiveness and this was the hardest name of them all to say but as the sound of my name rang out, the huge hedge crumbled and collapsed unto the pathway, reduced to a heap of broken sticks.

I leaped up, a new joy in my heart, a new release in my spirit and swept the sticks aside to reveal the path ahead. The Master came to my side and I set out once more to serve Him wherever He called me. I sought out my former companions and poured over our broken relationships the oil of my forgiveness. The Master nodded His approval, set His grace in our lives and put His peace in our hearts. And I knew that many times on our journey I would have to 'let go' and many times I would hear His command to forgive but I determined that never again would the hedge grow tall or the brambles block my path. After all, I had been forgiven much more than I would ever be required to forgive. I would learn to 'let go'.

PRODIGALS

You don't give up on prodigals, Father,
    That's so good to know.

I've been there, Father,
    Been a prodigal,
Taken myself off to a far country
Lived in the city of self,
Fed on my own resources
Till nothing was left
    And no one was there for me.

Running on empty – no joy, no peace, no love,
But emptiness cried out to be filled,
The memories flooded in
    the sound of Your voice
    the power of Your word
    the tenderness of Your touch
    the warmth of Your smile
And I just wanted to be home again.

You don't hold out on prodigals, Father,
    That's so good to know.

Acceptance is instant.
You don't wait to see how I'll shape up,
    Forgiveness is total.
You don't keep reminding me of where I've been
    Reinstatement is immediate.
I walk back into Your house again as a much – loved daughter,
    Love is absolute.
You regard me with the same delight as You did before I went away,
    Joy is unsurpassed.
You celebrate my coming with lavish generosity,
Clothe me in fresh garments and new shoes,

Throw a party for me.

I'm not so good with prodigals, Father,
       Give me Your heart for them.

I would give up on them,
I would hold out on them.

Somehow I seem to think
They need to be punished
Or, at the very least, set to one side.
I need them to prove themselves
Show their sincerity.
I greet their repentance with scepticism
       their return with suspicion.
Somehow they aren't just as valuable as they were before.

Show me Your heart for the prodigals, Father:
       a heart of compassion
              acceptance
              tolerance
              love and joy.

Help me to go running to meet them
       Even when they are still a long way off
Keep reminding me that I was once a prodigal.

I will exalt You O Lord,
*   for You lifted me out of the depths.*

Psalm 30 v 1

CHAPTER 13
LIFTED

The day began like any other in Kingdom Park. A red and orange sunrise lent colour to the day for a few brief minutes, unseen by many who preferred to snuggle down under a warm duvet to snatch a final moment of rest before the busyness of the day caught up with them. As I walked along, my heart rejoiced that the King would arrange such a spectacular display for the eyes of so few. He was indeed an extravagant King.

Soon I became aware that a river ran beside the road – I could hear its singing as the water rushed over the stones on the river bed.

"The cool water will refresh my aching feet," I thought as I clambered down the bank. It was a pretty river, its water clear and not too deep. I took off my shoes and began to paddle, my feet sinking a little into the muddy river bed.

"Ouch," I shouted as my toe caught the edge of a submerged rock and immediately the Master was at my side.

"You've forgotten again!" He rebuked me gently. "If you let Me lead, I'll show you where to place your feet and warn you of the hidden dangers."

I rubbed my throbbing toe and smiled ruefully.

"It does take a long time for the lessons You teach me to sink in," I agreed as I moved aside to allow Him to lead the way.

We followed the river as it made its way between two interlocking spurs. The hills of Kingdom Park might be hard to climb but the wonderful scenery was worth the effort. All around me were mountain slopes dressed in the rich colours of Autumn. Red, brown and golden foliage glowed in the morning sun and sheep grazed contentedly in the grassy fields.

"This is going to be a perfect day," I breathed. "Sun is shining, glorious landscape to enrich my soul and You beside me – perfect."

The Master gave a quick glance at the sky and His reply didn't quite match up to my enthusiasm.

"Let's just enjoy it while it lasts," He said cautiously. "You never know what might be ahead in Kingdom Park."

As He spoke, the sun disappeared behind a cloud and I shivered as a cool breeze rustled the leaves of the trees on the riverbanks. I made my way round a bend in the river and very quickly found that the water which had just covered my ankles before now lapped at my knees.

"How strange," I thought, "the river should be getting more shallow as I climb up into the hills, not getting deeper."

But the Master still walked with me and I felt safe in His Presence so I continued on my journey. Then, without any warning at all, the sky was split by a massive bolt of lightning, thunder rumbled and echoed from hill to hill and the heavens opened, soaking me in a heavy downpour. The next moment I heard a mighty roar of rushing water and I looked up to see what looked like a great wall of water about to engulf me.

I knew instantly what had happened – the storm had caused a flash flood further up the valley and it was coming my way! Forgetting all about the Master, I made for the bank, stumbling over the hidden rocks and almost losing my balance in the rushing water which was now up to my waist. Terror and sheer determination gave me strength and I clambered over to the bank, clutching at little bushes and clumps of grass in a desperate attempt to pull myself out. But the river was too strong and I felt myself slipping back into the water. Then I remembered the Master.

"Help me!" I screamed. "I can't do this on my own! Get me out of the flood!"

In the same moment, I felt His hand holding my head above the water but instead of helping me out of the river, He pulled me to the place where I had run from Him.

"What are you doing?" I shouted above the noise of thunder and rushing water. "I'm afraid! I want out of here!"

The Master held me securely in the middle of the flood which was now so high that I could barely keep my feet on the river bed.

"You need to learn, Child," He said, "that you are safer here with Me in the flood than on the bank on your own."

Even though He spoke quietly, somehow His words penetrated the sounds all around me.

"Do you trust Me? Do you believe I can keep you safe in the storm?" He asked.

For a brief moment I searched my heart. I glanced quickly at the bank that seemed to be the only place of safety and then I felt once more the tenderness in the firm grip of His hand as He held my head above the flood.

"Yes," I whispered, "I trust You. I believe………."

The end of the sentence never got spoken for at that very moment, a wave of water broke over my head and I felt myself go under. I could no longer cry out to Him, I could no longer see His face but by some miracle, I could still hear His voice.

"Fear not………..you are Mine…………….When you're in over your head, I'll be there with you. When you're in rough waters, you will not go down."

The words calmed my racing heart and a strange peace

descended upon me. It didn't matter any more that I might drown. I was willing to abandon myself to His will.

Suddenly, I felt a mighty hand grip me and pull me, slowly but firmly out of the flood waters. What power, what strength, what comfort there was in that grip. My feet touched something flat and solid and I opened my eyes to see the Master smiling at my shocked expression.

"What happened? What was that?" I asked in complete bewilderment, as I looked around and realised that though the flood waters were still rushing past, I had been lifted above them and was standing on a stepping stone in the middle of the river.

"That was the Hand of the King," replied the Master. "He knows all that goes on in Kingdom Park. He knows when His people are drowning and sometimes He just reaches down His Hand and sets them on a rock. He is the King, even of the flood. He saw your faith. He loves those who are abandoned to My will. You didn't know about the stepping stones in the river, but He did."

I looked down and saw that, from one bank to the other, a set of flat stepping stones had been planted in the river.

"Now take my hand," said the Master, "all you have to do is to take one step at a time and you'll get safely to the other side."

The storm continued to rage around me and the flood waters still rushed down the valley and now and then I could even feel the water splash against my feet as waves broke against the stepping stones. But I was no longer afraid. I was in a place of safety and I knew I would make it to the bank. And I knew too that I would always remember the firmness of the Hand that had rescued me from the flood – the Hand of the King of the flood.

BROKENNESS

Is brokenness required, my Lord?
I know it was, for You.
But do I have to suffer, Lord,
Is pain my pathway too?

I know it was for Jacob, Lord,
His blessing came through pain,
A damaged limb came with God's touch,
He'd never be the same again.

I find it hard to think of Job,
His pain makes mine seem small.
God did restore what he had lost,
But only after losing all.

There is a fellowship of pain,
That sometimes is God's plan
To draw His people close to Him,
Mysterious bond of God and man.

For somehow in the broken heart,
His voice is heard – so loud, so clear,
His words bring comfort, strength and grace,
Assure me that my God is near.

So in this time of brokenness,
Give me a listening ear,
Open my heart, despite the pain,
His touch to know, His voice to hear.

I will pour out My Spirit on all people.

Joel ch 2 v 28

CHAPTER 14
SPIRIT WATERFALL

They all had it – that indefinable something extra. The longer I lived in Kingdom Park, the more easily I could recognise it. There was a certain light in their eyes, an extra joy in their smile. They knew the Master in a way I didn't and I just couldn't work out where I was going wrong. I watched carefully to see if they walked differently or read the Book longer or talked more to the Master but those things couldn't explain the difference I sensed.

Eventually I plucked up enough courage to ask one of these pilgrims to explain what I had observed. She gave a shy smile and said, "It might be something to do with my visit to Spirit Waterfall."

I had heard others talk of Spirit Waterfall before, not always in a very positive way. The pilgrims who had walked along Tradition Road with me had warned me never to go there.

"It's not for us," they assured me. "You can read about it and even study it but don't ever go there."

Other pilgrims had been wildly enthusiastic about Spirit Waterfall but had spoken of it in such over excited, mysterious terms that I had been rather scared and had just put it all out of my mind.

"I know enough about the Great Spirit," I reasoned. "Didn't the Master explain to me about the Reservoir and I was happy to turn on the tap in my house and allow the Spirit to flow. I'm sure that's enough."

But all that day it had kept niggling at me. I asked another pilgrim in whom I had seen the indefinable something and immediately he knew what I was talking about.

"Oh," he said with great conviction, "going through the waterfall made all the difference in my life in Kingdom Park. In fact, I go there as often as I can."

By now I was confused – I longed more than ever to have what these pilgrims had but the warnings I had heard still echoed in my ears. Would it displease the King if I journeyed to Spirit Waterfall? Was it safe to go there?

I decided to ask the Master and as always, He was right by my side and as always, His words were wisdom itself.

"The Book has much to teach you about the Great Spirit. Other pilgrims have written about Him too. Spend some time just finding out about Him and if you want to go to Spirit Waterfall, I'll take you there."

So I heeded His advice and spent the next few months reading as much as I could and listening to many pilgrims who were only too happy to tell of their own visits to Spirit Waterfall. And the longing in my heart grew in intensity and a hunger for this 'more' consumed me until at last I simply said,

"Master, I'm ready. Take me to the Waterfall."

He took me by the hand and led me along a new path. We climbed high into the hills and I heard the roar of the waterfall long before I saw it. My heart beat faster at the mighty sound of the rushing water but whether it was excitement or fear that caused it to race, I couldn't tell.

We followed the sound, skirted a rocky outcrop and suddenly there it was before me in all its splendour – Spirit Waterfall. The sight took my breath away. I had seen waterfalls before but nothing like this. I looked up to see the top of the cliff – every waterfall I had ever seen before had flowed over a cliff edge or down a steep mountain side but this waterfall had no such beginning – it came from so far away that clouds obscured my vision. I looked down to see where the water touched the earth but so great was its height that I could see only mist and spray below. The whole waterfall hung like a curtain between the mountains, a shimmering, sparkling, rushing, living torrent of water. It poured down with such force, such tremendous power that I stepped back in fear, shouting at the Master over its roar.

"The pilgrims said they walked through the Waterfall. Surely not! They couldn't have! It's too strong, it's too big!"

The Master smiled reassuringly.

"They all survived," he said and looked at me with a question in His eyes.

"Oh, I'm not too sure about this," I whispered uncertainly. "I don't think I can do it."

"Just go as close as you can," He encouraged me. "You can always step back if it is too overwhelming."

So I gathered my courage and inched along the path that led into the waterfall. I was astonished to find that the closer I went to the water, the less noisy and forceful it seemed to become.

I felt the spray on my face first of all – it was cool and refreshing and felt like the smoothest silk on my skin. And suddenly the fear was gone and there was just joy, sheer joy. I walked on into the mighty waterfall and found that far from being pounded by a powerful force of falling water, I seemed to have entered a gentle rain. It fell like Irish rain, soft and light against my arms and legs. I lifted my face up to it, surrendering to its touch, sensing that here was healing and refreshing and renewal. Tears flowed freely and mingled with the rain on my cheeks – tears of joy and tears of longing – a stirring of emotion I had never before experienced.

Afterwards I found it impossible to work out how long I had stayed in Spirit waterfall, singing and worshipping, crying and laughing and dancing and I never fully understood exactly what had happened there. All I could say was that I had been touched in some deep hidden part of my being by the Great Spirit.

When I eventually stepped out of the waterfall, it was to discover that I had somehow entered a new realm in Kingdom Park and everything had changed. I walked differently, I worshipped differently, I served the King differently. When I read the Book, its words had deeper meaning and now, when the Master drew near, my heart just sang for joy and felt as though at any moment it might burst with longing – a longing to know Him and to know the King and to be constantly bathed in the rain of the Great Spirit.

AND THEN HE CAME

And then He came,
To touch my my life
With gentle hand
And all-embracing love.

I bowed in wonder at His coming
That He, the One enthroned in realms eternal,
Whose robes are light, who lives in glorious majesty,
Should come with outstretched hand to me.

I saw the beauty of His coming –
And knew His peace that passes understanding,
That sweet tranquility, that calm serenity,
That other-worldliness that words cannot describe.

I felt the glory of His coming –
The Spirit's mighty resurrection power,
Transformed to touch the fabric of my life,
Gentle to suit my frailty, powerful enough to speak His Name.

Sweet Spirit, You have come
And touched my life
With gentle hand
And all-embracing love.

So I would sing my sweetest songs to God the Lord,
And bow in awe and worship at His feet,
Pour out the love that wells up from within,
Take great delight in fellowship so sweet.
But what I've seen and known is just a little thing,
A tiny window into Heaven above,
When I will know His power without restraint,
And spend eternity in all-embracing love.

They shall soar on wings like eagles.

Isaiah ch 40 v 31

CHAPTER 15
LIKE AN EAGLE

The Master beckoned me to follow Him.

"Come," He said "there's something I want to show you." I had learned the value of following closely where He led so I scrambled to my feet and fell into step beside Him.

At first the incline was gentle and the grassy meadows were soft under my feet but it wasn't long before the path grew steeper and I began to feel the sharpness of the stones even through the strong boots on my feet. I stumbled more and more frequently but each time His hand reached out to support and strengthen me and each time I found the courage to go on.

As the day wore on, I grew weary. My legs ached, my back was sore, my feet were blistered. The path was difficult to follow, over the hillocks, around enormous boulders across icy mountain streams, always climbing relentlessly upwards. There were moments when it seemed to vanish altogether and I hesitated, unsure of where to put my feet. At those uncertain times, I would hear the Master's voice, "Keep close to Me. I'll tell you where to walk."

When it seemed as though we had been climbing forever, I begged the Master for a rest. "Where are we going? Why is the road so hard?"

He smiled and pointed with His finger. My eyes looked in the direction He had indicated and my heart sank.

"Up there?" I asked. My voice was flat with despair. "I can't do it. It's too high. The path is too rough. I just can't go on."

The Master didn't seem to be surprised by my outburst.

"Listen child," He whispered. "I know you have learned to keep close to Me. That's good but you're still trying to walk in your own strength. Learn to lean on Me more. Use My strength to climb the mountain. If you lean on Me, you can use My energy to sustain you. Come, take My arm."

So. rather tentatively at first, but with increasing confidence, I put my arm in His and leaned on the Master. I was amazed to discover that what had seemed an insurmountable rock face, was no longer impossible to conquer. It was still hard work, but step by step we climbed together to the ledge He had indicated to me.

I clambered onto the rocky outcrop and sat down to get my breath back. We were high up in the mountains where the air was clear and pure and the clouds drifted lazily over the summit. I looked down into the valley and realised that it was so easy now to see the path we had followed. The tortuous twists and turns the Master had taken made perfect sense as I looked back on them.

"Is this why you have brought me here - to show me that Your way is best?" I asked.

"No child," came the gentle reply, "I know that for many years you have acknowledged the wisdom of My ways. What I want to show you is just over there."

Nestling near the edge of the ledge I could see a large nest, an eagle's nest. In the nest were three eaglets, cheeping noisily at the sky. As I watched, a great eagle swooped from the clouds and called to his offspring. The cheeping became more frantic, then two of the baby birds shuffled to the side of the nest, clambered over, then clumsily hopped to the edge of the outcrop. With hardly a hesitation they flung themselves into the air, wings flapping madly to gain altitude. Then all at once they caught an updraught of air, their wings ceased the frantic flapping and they soared effortlessly into the sky to dive and swoop with the great eagle.

The beauty of their flight entranced me and in a rare moment of insight, I understood why the Master had patiently encouraged me to the top of the mountain.

"That's what I long to do," I sighed. "I want to learn to soar. Walking close and leaning on Your arm are wonderful but they're not enough. I know there is more. I want to soar but I don't know how and I'm just a bit afraid. I'm afraid of taking that step into the unknown."

"I know," came the reply, "I've seen the longing in your heart. Now, watch what happens to the third eaglet."

I had forgotten about the other little bird but now I looked to see what had happened to him. He was still in the nest, gazing longingly at the sky and cheeping furiously. He kept making darting little runs to the other side of the nest but never quite made it over the rim. The great eagle flew close by and called again and this time the tiny eaglet stumbled out of the nest on to the ledge. He went right over to the edge and stood there shivering. He looked up into the sky, then down into the deep valley, flapped his wings as though to try them out, then just sat down at the edge of the rock, seemingly content just to watch as his brothers soared high up into the sky.

"Oh I know just how he feels," I breathed. "It's hard to leave the safety of the ledge. He's not sure if it will work for him - maybe his wings won't be strong enough, maybe he'll find that he can't fly and he'll plummet into the valley below."

Then the insistent call of the great eagle came again and the little one ran to the edge and launched himself into the sky. His wings beat the air frantically and he began to gain height. Then all at once he lost rhythm and began to fall helplessly down into the valley.

"He's falling," I cried. "He isn't strong enough! He'll be hurt!"

"Keep watching," said the Master with a smile.

Suddenly the rhythmic beat of mighty wings could be heard as the majestic shape of the great eagle moved through the sky. He dived below the falling eaglet and gently caught the little one on his wing, depositing him on the ledge to recover from his ordeal.

I breathed a sigh of relief, then turned to the Master as He began to speak. "There's nothing to fear, you see. The Father watches every move and even if you fall and fail to soar, He'll spread His mighty wings and raise you up once more."

Again the great eagle's call rent the sky and I watched the little eaglet answer that call once more. This time he flung himself off the edge with greater confidence and I saw with delight that almost immediately he began to soar upwards. He had caught the thermal, he was riding the wind.

I felt an intense longing arise within me as I watched the little bird circle ever higher and higher to join his brothers. The Master's voice broke in on my thoughts.

"You want to soar? Then listen for the Father's call, wait for His voice and when you hear it, step out without fear - you will soar on wings like eagles as the wind of the Spirit catches you up. Your destiny is not in the safety of the nest, but the freedom of the skies. You have learnt to walk close to Me, to lean on My strength, even to sing in the shadows of life but now the time has come to soar. Come, child, let His voice encourage you to fly ever higher with Him. His sweet presence will attend all your ways and His mighty wings will ever be outstretched to protect you. His love be your everlasting portion and His goodness and mercy will follow you all the days of your life. When you soar with Him, your vision will be broadened as you see things from the Father's perspective, and your insight into His truth will be deepened.

Come. it's time to soar on wings like the eagle."

SOARING

I looked up from the valley,
Saw an eagle flying high.
I watched him swoop and dive with ease
Soar on thermals in the sky.

How effortless his movement seemed,
How far afield his view.
I longed to soar on outstretched wings
But valley paths were all I knew.

Then the Master's voice called, "Come,
Let My Spirit carry you.
He'll teach you how to soar above,
He'll refresh, anoint, renew."

My heart held back in fear,
Afraid to trust what I couldn't see.
I hid inside my comfort zone,
But His voice still called to me.

Till one day I stood at the edge,
Determined to fear no more,
I fell at first, felt His Spirit's wings
Lift me high and help me to soar.

I still walk the paths in the valley
But I know what it means to soar.
Each time I surrender my will to His,
I catch the wind of His Spirit once more.

*May the God of hope
     fill you with all joy and peace
        as you trust in Him.*

Romans ch 15 v 13

CHAPTER 16
THE GOLDEN STRAND

"I have a treat for you today," said the Master with a smile.

"I'm sure there will be hard lessons to go along with it," I thought.

He knew what I was thinking and gently reassured me,

"No hard lessons – just sheer joy!"

"I'm sorry," I said ruefully, "I keep forgetting that You know my thoughts. It's rather disconcerting, You know!"

"I do know," He replied, "but isn't it great that you don't always have to articulate exactly how you feel? I understand your sighs and your desires and hear even the faintest whisper of your heart."

I nodded my agreement and then realised that while we had been talking, the path had been changing from the smooth surface we had been travelling on for so long, to a narrow, grassy, sandy track. I loved walking on sand and stopped to take off my shoes so that I could feel the warm, soft sand beneath my bare feet.

As we began to climb what I recognised to be a sand dune, I heard in the distance a wonderfully familiar sound – the distinctive sound of waves breaking on a shore. My heart raced with excitement and I grasped at the thick grasses to pull myself up to the top of the dune.

"Oh," I shouted, "You were right – this is sheer joy! I didn't know there was a shoreline in Kingdom Park. This will be my favourite place in the entire land – I just know it will!"

I stood for a moment drinking in the beauty and magnificence of the golden strand that lay before me. To my left and right, the line of sand dunes stretched for miles, providing the perfect backdrop to the long, deserted beach. The seagulls swooped and dived above the waves that broke in rushing lines of white foam on the shoreline. I filled my lungs with deep breaths of air – air that seemed fresher and purer than anywhere else in Kingdom Park.

I turned in delight to the Master.

"This place makes me feel like a child again!" I cried. "I want to race up and down the sand dunes, I want to paddle in the sea, I want to let the warm, fine sand trickle through my fingers…….."

"Then do it!" encouraged the Master. "This is a day of joy. Be a child again!"

"Are You sure it's OK?" I enquired anxiously. "What about serving You and helping others? I do want to please the King. I'm a bit apprehensive about giving myself over to sheer joy."

"But it will please the King to see your joy," the Master replied. "Go on – don't hold back!"

So I stood for a moment, unable to decide what to do first but the call of the waves was too strong to resist so I ran to the shoreline. I caught my breath initially as the cool water lapped over my feet but my body soon adjusted to the temperature as I ran in and out of the tiny waves. I lifted my face to the sun and felt its warmth soothe and relax me. I closed my eyes and listened to the sound that since early childhood had held the power to entrance – the gentle thunder of breaking waves as one by one they reared and curled and fell in a sparkling crash of pure white foam. Such joy!

The waves further out beckoned me and I slowly ploughed my way towards them, turning my back at the last moment to allow one to break over me. I laughed aloud in delight. It was exhilarating and refreshing and my heart just sang with joy as the power of the waves pushed me firmly back to the edge of the water. I skipped and danced among the tiny waves in the shallows, lifting up my voice in a song of praise and it seemed in those joy-filled moments, that the Master was closer than He had ever been before, that He too was skipping and dancing at the water's edge, that somehow I felt His joy as He enjoyed mine.

I shivered as a little breeze tugged at my damp clothes and so I decided to run through the sand hills to dry off. As I ran with childish abandon into the hollow behind the first row of dunes, I was struck, as I had been many times before, by the silence and the stillness. The breeze couldn't follow me into the hollow and the sound of the breakers faded to a distant whisper. There was a near-monastic feel in the grassy, sandy hollow – cut off from the rest of Kingdom Park, from its people and its noise.

I chose a little hillock that faced the sun and sat down, wriggling in the soft sand to make a perfectly fitting armchair for myself. Here was a place where I could think clearly, a place where I could worship easily. As I waited in the silence and solitude, it seemed that the Master had moved closer still. I had delighted in the closeness of His Presence in the dancing waves but this was a different nearness. Here I knew His Presence within me and His voice rose and fell with ease and clarity in my mind. He took my thoughts captive and held them focussed on Him. What joy – joy upon joy!

I stretched out my arm, lifted a handful of the fine sand and watched with wonder as the tiny grains trickled out between my fingers. It felt smooth and silky and I marvelled at the amazing process of the sea that had reduced the mighty rock of some distant cliff to the grains that tickled my palm.

"Why does a golden strand fill me with such joy?" I wondered and waited in the silence until the Master's answer flowed through my thinking as His Spirit communed with my spirit.

"The Father made it so. He formed both the beauty and your capacity to enjoy it. He arranged it so that blue skies and sparkling seas and golden sand and dancing waves would call forth immense delight within you – at first on a purely physical level."

"But there is also a spiritual dimension that you recognise deep in your soul. Everything here speaks of spiritual things. The Great Sea reminds you of eternity – you can only see as far as the horizon but you know it stretches far beyond the line where sea and sky meet."

"The great mystery of how something so seemingly fragile as water has the power to crush rock and reduce it to boulders, pebbles and sand, reminds you of the power of the Great Spirit who works unceasingly to shape and mould you to please the King."

"The waves that constantly break on the shore but which obey some invisible boundary so they don't overwhelm the land, demonstrates how the Father has lovingly set boundary lines in your life as well so that the enemy cannot overwhelm you."

"The cries of the seagulls tell you that the Father has given you a song too – a song that you can use in worship, a song that brings great delight to His heart."

"The rising tide that cleanses the beach, deposits sand particles with its swash and removes other sand particles with its backwash teaches you how the Great Spirit works in the Kingdom and encourages you to watch for the high tides – to be ready for the deposits they will leave behind in the Kingdom, deposits of signs and wonders and miracles; to be prepared for the cleansing that will come with His high tide; to be undismayed when the tide goes out once again, knowing that some day it will come again."

As He spoke of the high tide of the Great Spirit, I was startled by the intensity of the longing that rose within me – a longing that in my generation, His high tide would sweep in on to the shore of Kingdom Park and my spirit cried out for it to be so.

"Keep that longing alive in your heart," He whispered softly.

"Your desire rises up like sweet incense to the throne of the Great King. Pray that His response will come soon – a mighty surge of the Spirit sweeping all over Kingdom Park."

I returned a little later to the top of the sand dune and watched as the sun set over the sea. Its multicoloured splendour was the perfect ending to a day of joy and I breathed a prayer of thanks to the Master who had called me to follow and had presented me with such a gift. Sheer joy He had promised – sheer joy it had been!

YOUR TOUCH

Your touch has opened up a spring
Of great delight, unceasing praise,
Rushing from a central core of joy
To flow unchecked through all my days.
And words are not enough, Dear Lord
So take my tongue to serve Your will
And sounds unknown, unsought, unheard
Will echo through my head and fill
My mouth with songs of praise.
My dancing heart joins in the song
Of love and deep, exhilarating joy
And all day long and all night long
Its rhythm calls me back to You,
The Awesome One whose touch I crave,
Whose love pours out upon my soul
And bathes me in His mighty, joyous wave.

You found me in the wilderness,
An empty, windswept land,
Made me the apple of Your eye,
Lavished love with generous hand.
Hovered like an eagle wild,
Then taking flight into the sky,
You lifted me on mighty wings
And taught me how to fly.
You set me on the mountain top,
Fed my soul the richest meal
From rocks and crags produced for me
Honey to sweeten and oil to heal.

And so today I make my vow –
I'll not break faith, I'll heed Your Word,
Declare that I'll give honour to
The Holy Presence of my Lord.

Deut ch 32

CHAPTER 17
LEAVES IN AUTUMN

"Let Me show you one of My favourite scenes in the kingdom," said the Master with such anticipation in His voice that I left what I had been doing and followed eagerly in His footsteps. It was Autumn once more and as we walked, the fallen leaves crunched beneath our feet.

We followed the trail into a forested area and soon I was surrounded on every side by tall, majestic trees. The distinctive scent of pine pervaded the air and sounds from beyond the forest were silenced by the density of the trees. I glanced at the Master, wondering in my heart if these magnificent trees were what He had been so enthusiastic about – trees that stayed tall and green all year round.

He smiled and, as usual, read my mind.
"No, we still have some way to go," He answered my unspoken question.

Some time later, we reached a clearing in the forest, a huge, roughly circular grassy area. I walked into the centre of this arena and sat down on a moss-covered tree stump. As I breathed in the perfume of grass and trees, I closed my eyes and felt my shoulders fall and my whole body relax. What a wonderful place – a green space protected by the tall green trees of the forest – quiet and so peaceful.
"This is like a great, natural cathedral," I thought. "I could worship the King here. Surely this is what He wanted to show me."

*There is a time for everything
and a season for every activity
under Heaven.*

Ecclesiastes ch 3 v 1

When I opened my eyes, the Master was smiling but also shaking His head.

"You're right in one respect," He told me. "This is a place where you might encounter the King and it would indeed be easy to worship Him here in the stillness. But it's not where I'm leading you today."

I rose from the tree stump and somewhat reluctantly followed the Master out of the clearing and back into the comparative darkness of the forest. The path twisted and turned as it snaked up the hillside and I kept stumbling over tree roots that had broken through the surface. It wasn't long before I was feeling tired and I longed to be back in the clearing.

"I'm not as young as I used to be," I grumbled to the Master. "It's all very well for the young ones to be taken trekking high in the forest but I don't have the energy for a steep climb like this."

He moved closer to my side and drew my arm through His.

"Let's do it together," He encouraged. "It's not much further and it will be worth it in the end."

Within a few moments, we had crested a ridge and there spread out before us was a long valley filled almost entirely by a lake. As we walked down the hill, a gentler slope on this side of the ridge, I became aware that we were no longer surrounded by evergreen trees but by deciduous trees, whose leaves were responding to the call of Autumn by changing colour.

The Master found a fallen log near the water's edge and we sat down together.

"This is what I wanted to show you" He said softly, "the glory of the trees in Autumn. Sit for a moment and savour the beauty."

What a sight met my eyes. The leaves of the tree under which I sat were like burnished bronze, while the one next to it was covered in deep orange, almost red leaves. Nearby, the bright yellow leaves of a chestnut tree waved gently in the breeze, while yet another tree beside it was dressed in foliage of bright pink. The entire lake was encircled in similar displays of such beauty that they took my breath away. The dazzling scene was reflected in the still water of the lake, redoubling the effect and where the sun shone, the colours glowed even brighter.

It was one of those moments in Kingdom Park that I wanted to hold on to, the memory of which would bring solace when I had to face a dark day. Then the Master began to speak and His words burned deep into my soul.

"You said on the way here that you're not as young as you used to be – well that is partly why I wanted you to see the splendour of this scene and learn the lesson of the leaves in Autumn. These leaves have been hard at work since Spring – taking in sunlight and rain and playing a vital role in helping the tree to grow. Now they are changing colour and it may seem that their work is over."

"Oh yes," I interrupted, "that's just how I feel sometimes and I know my friends feel like that too now and again. We have worked hard in Kingdom Park but we don't have the energy to do what we used to do. Sometimes it feels as though we have lost our value, that we're a bit useless now."

"Tell Me," asked the Master with a twinkle in His eye, "how did the Autumn leaves make you feel when I showed them to you?"

"They made my heart sing with delight – they were so beautiful," I replied.

"Well, Child," the Master informed me, "that's how the King feels when He looks at you in this Autumn season. You may not have the strength to work as hard for the Kingdom but you can be beautiful, more beautiful than at any other time in your life. And it gives great pleasure to the King when He sees you putting on a dazzling display for His glory."

I did feel better for a moment or two as I gazed once more at the glowing colours but then a sadness rose from deep within me. Those beautiful leaves would soon die and fall from the trees and they reminded me of my own mortality. The Master sensed my change of mood and moved closer to reassure me.

"It's not the end for the leaves when they die, you know," He whispered.

"When they fall and decay, they create nourishing food for the future life of the tree, food for future leaves and food for future fruit. In a similar way, the things you say and do will live on after you, providing nourishing food to help future generations to live and grow and produce fruit – like a rich spiritual compost!"

I laughed at the thought of being compost and the Master laughed with me, then He added,

"Autumn does lead to the dark, cold days of Winter. It can be a time of loss and emptiness and harsh circumstances but don't fear it. I'll be just as close to you in Winter as in the bright, sunny days of Summer – maybe even a little closer! Every Winter holds the promise of Spring, the promise of rebirth, renewal and new life."

A great smile lit up His face, a smile that spoke of secret knowledge and deep mysteries.

"You have no idea what the Spring will be like – such wonder, such riches…….. everything made new……… being able to look on the face of the King ………. So don't fear the Winter that leads you there."

"And Child," he went on, His voice resonating with joy and delight. "some leaves get the chance to fly before they fall – carried along by the wind, twirling and turning in an exciting dance, soaring high into the sky. Some of them manage to fly a long way and even create compost for other trees in the forest."

I caught some of His enthusiasm and my heart beat faster. Maybe Autumn in Kingdom Park would turn out to be the most exciting season of them all! Maybe I too could put on a spectacular display for the King, glowing with the brightest colours, bringing glory to His Name and pleasure to his heart. And maybe, just maybe, I would get to fly as I yielded my life to the wind of His Spirit, soaring and dancing as He carried me through Winter into His eternal Spring.

THE ALABASTER BOX

The woman loved her Lord
Love welled up deep within.
She searched for days to find a way
To show her love for Him.

Two days before the feast, the answer came.
With sudden clarity she knew,
To give expression to her love –
Only her very best would do.

She hurried to her secret place,
Unwrapped the precious box with care,
Held it while she searched her heart
Could she her treasure share?

But love is a compelling force,
No other action would suffice,
The Master's words had changed her life –
With joy she'd make this sacrifice.

She quickly ran to Simon's house,
The Lord was dining there.
With love for Jesus in her eyes,
She broke her box of ointment rare.

The fragrance of the ointment rose
And filled the house with perfume sweet.
She poured it on her Master's head,
Then knelt in worship at His feet.

Suddenly the woman cringed –
Harsh cries of protest filled her ears.
"It is a waste", "A shameful thing" –
Her smiles of love and worship turned to tears.

She hardly dared to raise her eyes
To look into the Master's face –
Would He agree? Send her away?
Call her act of worship a disgrace?

She waited with her eyes downcast,
Then Jesus placed His hand upon her head,
"What she has done was beautiful,
Leave her alone," He said.

And as the Master leaned across
To raise her to her feet,
Tiny droplets touched the woman
Bathed her in perfume sweet.

She left Him then, but all that day
The fragrance filled the air.
She breathed it in and knew again
His love and tender care.

So may my worship be
A sacrificial gift of love.
And may the Master touch my life,
His oil anoint me from above.

*Even though I walk
 through the valley of the shadow of death,
 I will fear no evil.*

Psalm 23 v 4

CHAPTER 18
SHADOW VALLEY

My journey through Kingdom Park varied almost every day. Sometimes I walked on straight roads with good surfaces and well maintained edges. On other days the path was uneven and potholed. Now and again the Master and I followed a winding river to its source high in the mountains, then on the other side, the path sloped down through dense forests into the valley below.

I loved the valleys – it was usually easier to walk in the valley. The lush grass was soft under my aching feet and the wild flowers that grew in the fields brought delight to my soul as they spoke of the Father's creative heart. Many animals and birds made their homes in the valleys and as I watched them engaged in the life designed for them by the Great Creator, the Master taught me many lessons about how I could fulfil my purpose in Kingdom Park. I was awakened by birdsong each daybreak and as the birds sang in worship to the Father, so I was encouraged to lift my heart in worship too. I observed even the tiniest animals instinctively caring for their young and it spoke to me of the tender love and protective care of the Father.

But then I came to Shadow Valley. It seemed at first to be like any other valley though I did notice that there were no flowers in the fields and thought that was a little strange. Then out of the corner of my eye I saw something (or was it someone?) move in the trees beside the path. I turned to look properly but all I could see was something grey, something shadowy, something that seemed to be following me.

Although it was indistinct, elusive, it was enough to make me feel threatened. My heart skipped a beat and I sensed the first stirrings of fear. As I often did when fear came calling at my door, I whispered the Master's name.

"I'm here," He said.

I waited for Him to speak again but He said no more. Reassured by His Presence, I moved on again but the road took a steep dip downwards and I stumbled, falling off the edge of the path.

There was no soft grass in this valley to cushion my fall and I cried out as nettles stung every piece of bare skin they could find and brambles tore at my clothing.

"Help me Master!" I screamed. "What sort of a place is this? Get me out of here! I'm hurting all over!"

Even before I stopped shouting, I felt His arm reach in through the stinging nettles. He freed me from the tangle of brambles, set me back on the path and poured His special balm over the rash caused by the nettles. I searched His face for an answer to my question – what sort of a place could this be?

"This is Shadow Valley," He said. "Many pilgrims walk this way."

I looked along the path I had been following but could see no one else.

"Oh you won't see other pilgrims," He told me, knowing what I was thinking in my heart. "Each pilgrim follows a separate path."

I thought how much easier it would be to have the company of at least one other pilgrim but the Master just looked at me and said once again,

"I'm here."

Again I waited for Him to speak but He said no more.

We walked on a little further and as the road sloped downwards even more steeply, I sensed a change in the temperature. By now we were in a wooded area and the trees overhead blocked out the light and the warmth of the sun so it became darker and colder. I couldn't see the path clearly and my limbs ached and my back hurt. How I wished I could leave this dark, cold place.

I shivered and drew the warm blanket of His grace more tightly around me. Suddenly my heart began to pound as the grey shadowy figure stepped out from the trees and came close beside me. Although indistinct and faceless, the figure brought such terror to my heart that I could only assume that Death himself had come near. I remembered then that the Book had spoken of the Valley of the Shadow of Death – Shadow Valley.

All thoughts of the Master's Presence fled and my only instinct was to escape. I turned to run from the shadowy figure, to flee from this dark valley but when I tried to retrace my steps, I found my way blocked. The nettles and brambles had sprung up behind me once again to form an impenetrable barrier.

I sank to my knees in despair – how could I face this valley? Why must I walk through it alone? My heart was filled with such fear of what lay ahead for me – fear of the valley itself – the darkness, the coldness, the pain, the loneliness and fear of the shadowy figure – would he catch me in his grip, would I be able to take that journey into the unknown, into death itself?

I sensed the grey shadow move a little closer and in desperation I called out the Master's name. He was, as always, instantly at my side, though my tears prevented me from seeing Him too clearly and it seemed as though His voice was very far away.

"I'm here," He said.

I waited to hear more. Surely at my time of greatest need, surely in this dark valley, with the shadow of death so close to me, surely He would say more to me now? But I heard only the faintest whisper,

"I'm here."
He said no more…………….. But it was enough.

Slowly I stood to my feet and turned to face Shadow Valley. I took a step and the shadow of death stepped with me but this time I spoke to that shadowy figure and told him,
"He's here. The Master walks with me. I will fear no evil."

As I spoke the words, I became more aware of the Master's Presence. I sensed His mighty arm holding me so that I couldn't fall into the nettles and brambles that encroached ever more fiercely on the path. His touch eased the pain and infused me with strength. His peace calmed my fear.

And so we journeyed – the pilgrim, the Master and the shadow of death. There were many difficult places in that valley – many days when pain filled my horizon; moments when death seemed inevitable and even attractive; times when the loneliness tore at my heart; long nights when I needed to sense His Presence and couldn't. But in each difficult place, His voice, however faint and far away, could still be heard, still saying only two words,
"I'm here."

I held on tightly to the promise of those two words all through that valley and sometimes they were all I had to cling to but they were enough. Then, one wonderful day, the shadowy figure moved away and I walked out into the light and warmth once again. As my steps took me further and further away from Shadow Valley, I sang out my praise to the One who had walked with me all through its darkness. And I knew that even should I have to follow its path another time, I would carry into its coldness and loneliness, the two words that had sustained me in my journey and I would hear again the Master's voice say,
"I'm here."

I'M HERE

I'm here to comfort you in sorrow,
I'm here to walk with you through pain,
I'm here to guide your faltering footsteps
To demonstrate My love again.

I'm here to give you My Shalom,
I'm here in every lonely place,
I'm here on days of desperation
To minister My lavish grace.

I'm here to put my arms around you,
I'm here to draw you very near,
I'll come each time you cry out 'Jesus'
To whisper once again 'I'm here'.

And surely I am with you always,
to the very end of the age.

Matthew ch 28 v 20

CHAPTER 19
CAVE OF DEPRESSION

It crept up on me, this feeling, little by little. I shrugged it off at first and when my fellow pilgrims remarked that I was very quiet and asked if anything was wrong, I just said I felt a bit under the weather but that I was fine, really. I noticed that the colours in Kingdom Park seemed to have faded a little, that the sky always seemed to be grey. In fact, as time went on, all of life seemed to be grey – a grey landscape.

Then one day I woke up feeling sad. I thought over the events of the previous day but could find no reason for my sadness. I examined my life but could find nothing that had changed, nothing that might have made me sad. I looked at the pilgrims walking at my side but they looked happy so they weren't the reason for my sadness. I just felt sad.

I decided it must have been just one of those mysterious things that happened now and again in Kingdom Park, listened to some music to lift my spirits and went on my way.

A few days later, I found it rather upsetting when the pilgrims who had been accompanying me veered off on a different path and I was left to walk alone.

"Never mind," I said to myself, "I'm not really alone anyway – the Master is always close by. I'll be fine. I can do this on my own."

The path led down into a bowl-shaped valley so walking was fairly easy.

"At least," I thought, "this isn't as bad as struggling up steep mountainsides and clambering over boulders to reach the summit."

The path didn't go straight down but spiralled down by following the curve of the valley's sides. As each circuit of the valley brought me lower, into the depths of the valley, I became aware that the air felt oppressive, like the air in a hot, humid jungle. I struggled to breathe and stopped by the side of the path.

"Master," I called out, "I'm turning back. I feel terrible. What is this place anyway?"

I sensed His Presence immediately but it seemed to me that He didn't come as close as He usually did and His voice, when He spoke, seemed muffled and unclear.

"I'm afraid………… no turning back…………." I thought I heard, "only way out………… through Cave of Depression……………..with you…………."

I remembered the hedges that had blocked my way when I tried to turn back before and realised that there was no point in even trying. Frantically I looked around for a way of escape – I didn't like the sound of the Cave of Depression! I wondered about leaving the path altogether and trying to hack my way through the undergrowth that covered the sides of the valley but it was too dense and early on in my journey, I had learnt the dangers of leaving the path. I didn't know what creatures might be lurking in the vegetation.

So, rather reluctantly, I set out once more along the path. I rounded the corner and there before me was the entrance to a huge cavern. It looked dark, damp and forbidding and I did not want to go inside.

"No, Master," I pleaded, "don't ask me to go in there. It's too frightening. Please, bring me out of this valley some other way!"

This time His voice was even less clear than before and seemed to come from far away.

"No...........way.................go through.............with you..........." was all I managed to hear.

So, very hesitantly, I went to stand in the gaping mouth of the cave. As I looked into the blackness, a fresh wave of sadness swept over my soul. I flung myself on the damp floor and wept bitterly. How could the Master allow this to happen? How did He expect me to find my way through this cave?

I wept all that day. Each time I thought that the crying had finished, despair rose up again and tears flowed freely. I hadn't thought it possible to weep so much – surely I had no tears left to cry?

It was even worse when evening fell. I watched the last rays of the sun set over the rim of the valley and fear rose up within, adding its weight to the crushing despair already in my heart.

"This must be the loneliest place in all of Kingdom Park," I thought.

I was totally alone. I could hear no sound of any living thing. No pilgrim's praises sang out, no prayers were said to comfort me, no one came to lift me up. And worst of all, there was no light.

I tried to cry out to the Master, to plead with Him to bring me light - even a tiny candle to dispel some of the darkness but no words would come. To my dismay I realised that I had lost the ability to use my weapon of Prayer.

"What about the Book?" I thought and began scrabbling around in the darkness to find where it had landed when I had fallen. I found it, clutched it to me, then realised with a great cry of despair, that it was too dark in the Cave to read its pages.

"Maybe it will be better when daylight comes," I thought. "Maybe I'll be able to find something in the Book that will help me through this terrible place."

When I awoke from a fitful sleep, I eagerly opened the Book in the faint light of early morning and began to read. I soon discovered that although I could read the words, I couldn't understand what the words meant. I wasn't even sure if I believed them any more. Faith seemed to have slipped away without me even knowing.

The overwhelming sadness I had known before welled up again. Despair and fear and loneliness took hold of me and once more I lay on the floor of the cave and cried. I couldn't understand what had gone wrong. Why could I not pray any more? Why could I not find comfort in the Book? Why did the journey I had made in Kingdom Park now seem unreal? If it was real, why did the Master not come and rescue me?

The sound was very faint but it was enough to make me raise my head and listen again.

"With you............with you........." It seemed to come from a great distance but it did sound like the Master's voice. A little spark of hope was ignited in my heart. He had always kept His word – could I trust Him to see me through this Cave of Depression? Would the faint promise of His Presence be enough when I had lost all sense of fellowship or communion with Him?

Slowly, I rose to my feet, dried my tears and took a few tentative steps into the darkness – a heavy, oppressive darkness. It seemed that I had no choice but to go on through this terrible Cave, I had heard others speak of Depression and its devastating effects but now I understood as I had never done before the despair and darkness they must have experienced.

Suddenly I heard someone shouting from the entrance to the cave. It was one of the pilgrims who had journeyed with me – I recognised his voice.

"Hello!" he called. "Can you hear me? Are you alright? Can I help you? I have my weapon of Prayer here!"

Although I knew that he felt only concern for me and that he would gladly use his weapon of Prayer on my behalf, I had neither the energy nor the inclination to reply to him. I just kept my back to him and stumbled on into the depths of the Cave. He waited for some moments then called again.

"I know you're there. I know how awful it is. I will pray for you."

"Pray if you like," I thought, "but it probably won't do any good."

In some deep place in my heart, I was aware that my negative thoughts weren't good, that the Enemy was using them to deepen my despair but I didn't have the strength to stand against him. The tears fell again – this time tears of weakness and hopelessness.

And so began a period in my journey through Kingdom Park that I wished I could have avoided. The days followed a similar monotonous pattern of sadness and weeping, of emptiness and worthlessness, of fear and despair. The sleepless nights stretched endlessly into the darkness and left me exhausted, scarcely able to put one foot in front of the other. The weeks turned into months and the seasons passed me by. Depression consumed my life.

On many occasions I wished that the shadowy figure of Death, whom I had so feared in Shadow Valley, would come and take me. Surely Death would be better than this long, dark tunnel that seemed to have no end, this deep pit that seemed to have no bottom. But even as I called on Death to come, I remembered His voice and the faint promise 'With you……………' and somehow gathered enough strength to go on.

And then one day I caught a glimpse, just a brief glimpse, of light. It was far away in the distance but it brought such hope to my heart. Many weeks passed before I caught another glimpse but when it finally came, my expectations grew. Now I knew which way to face – I could follow the direction of the light. There was a new determination in my step – I would make it through the Cave!

The light was very faint in those early weeks and while sometimes the path led me upwards towards the light, at other times it dropped alarmingly quickly back into the depths of the Cave. The tears continued to flow, the heaviness stayed in my heart but now and again when I looked back at where I had been, it seemed blacker and more terrible than where I stood and that gave me some encouragement.

Then one day when I woke up, I didn't cry and sometime later I slept all night. That morning I went back to the Book again and to my great relief, the words made sense.

"I waited patiently for the Lord," I read, "He turned to me and heard my cry. He lifted me out of the slimy pit, out of the mud and mire."

I had indeed been in a slimy pit, deep in mud and mire.

"Turn to me and hear my cry," I called and how reassuring it was to sense the Master's Presence once more. It had been such a long time since I had known the sweetness of His nearness.

"Come, Child," He said and immediately I put my hand into His, I felt Him lift me up out of the Cave and into the light once again. He placed my feet on a rock and in some strange way, He was the rock and He held my feet securely so that I couldn't slip back into the terrible Cave of Depression again.

I felt Him touch my lips and, softly at first, I began to sing – a song that rose up from deep within me, a song I had never sung before, a new song of praise to the One who had rescued me. My song of joy poured out across the valley, carried on air that was no longer heavy and oppressive, but pure and clear.

Another song joined in with mine and I turned to see who was singing – it was the pilgrim who had promised to pray for me. His face just beamed with delight and when the song ended, he took my hand in his.

"I have prayed for you every day that you spent in the Cave. I have walked with you in spirit and now I can't help but join in your song of joy."

We journeyed together for a while and every so often we would look at each other, joy would rise in out hearts and the song of praise would pour forth again, a song of thanksgiving to the One who kept His promise.

"With you..........." He had said.

He had been................and He always would be!

GREY LANDSCAPE

The landscape of my heart has turned to grey,
Blue skies and sunlight seem so far away,
And tears, like rain, keep washing over me,
Drowning all I do in unaccustomed misery.

The tide of pain is unrelenting in its force
And like the tide, it has to run its course.
It rushes in sometimes, quite gently at the shore,
Then gathers force to crash and break once more.

I thought I knew what storm and wind were like,
Had heard the thunderbolt and felt the lightning strike,
But nothing can compare with this storm's might,
The darkness of its clouds extinguishes the light.

But in the dark, grey landscape of my heart,
Your voice has whispered, 'Come with Me apart,
You need no words – just gaze into My face,
I'll rock you gently in the rhythms of My grace.'

So here I am, Lord, face awash with tears,
I'm giving You my sadnesses, my fears.
Until the storm has passed, I'll hide in You,
And surely, sometime Lord, the grey will turn to blue?

CHAPTER 20
WINTER SEASON

I wasn't really prepared for how quickly Winter came to Kingdom Park. I had hoped that the beauty of Autumn would last for just a little longer. If truth be told, I was dreading Winter. It spoke of darkness, cold and death – a world in monochrome, stark outlines of bare branches against grey skies, faded flowers and dead leaves. It spoke of hardship and loneliness and I wanted none of it. I remembered how difficult it had been to walk through Shadow Valley and I imagined that Winter would just be one long dark valley too.

"Why does beauty have to fade?" I wondered, "and why does everything have to die?"

Even as the thoughts rushed into my mind, the Master drew near and His Presence comforted me.

"I can't answer your question fully" He said, "not until you have passed through Winter and have entered the Eternal Spring I promised you. But I have something to show you that may help you to understand a little better."

He indicated that I should come with Him and, as I had done many times before, I followed in His footsteps. We had been walking in a particularly beautiful part of Kingdom Park, an area where huge, snow-capped mountains towered over tree-lined lakes. I had marvelled at the amazing scenery – each corner we turned presented us with a new vista, another scene that rendered me speechless, breathtaking in its splendour.

"Seeing all this beauty fills me with a strange sense of longing,"

Father, I want those You have given Me
to be with Me where I am
and to see My glory.

John ch 17 v 24

I told the Master, as we paused for a moment to admire yet another mountain perfectly reflected in the still waters of the lake at its feet.

"If the Father made all this," I continued, voicing thoughts that had been in my mind for a long time, "then He must be even more amazing, even more beautiful than His creation. I long so much to see Him, see Him properly – not just the little glimpses He grants to us here in Kingdom Park. To see completely the One who made it all – what would that be like? I keep trying to imagine what the Creator is like but it's no good – my mind is too small."

The Master touched my arm to show that He understood my longing and smiled at the futility of my efforts to imagine the Great Creator.

"The beauty He has made does show something of His character," he agreed. "The strength and stability and majesty of the mountains, the vastness of the universe, the infinite variety of snowflake designs, the wonder of cells and molecules, the complexity of the human body all speak of His glory but it's like the image of the mountain you see reflected in the lake – it gives you a good idea of what the mountain is like but it's only a fleeting image, an upside-down, easily distorted image. It's a little out of focus, the edges are blurred and it only shows up clearly in good light when the water is calm."

I gave a little sigh of disappointment and then the Master reminded me of something I had read in the Book.

"Don't forget that I'm the exact representation of the Father. So the best way to get to know the Father is to keep close to Me. When you look in My face, you see the Father."

I had been so absorbed in the conversation that I hadn't really noticed that the path we were following had begun to climb and I was surprised to discover, as we walked out of the shadow of some trees, that we had reached the snowline. We had already passed a few heaps of melting snow at the side of the path and the heaps had gradually been getting larger but I was still unprepared for the sight that met my eyes as we entered the clearing.

We were now much closer to the top of the mountain and from where we stood, right to the peak, the ground was covered in glistening snow. In the distance I could see other peaks, all of them covered in the same blanket of white. I turned around to look behind me and was amazed to see similar snow-capped mountains. Dazzlingly white snow interspersed with black, jagged rock, set against a blue sky......... pure cool air....... a calm stillness and a deep silence – what an experience. I continued to turn, gazing at one mountain after another, in an attempt to soak in the beauty, to store it up for a future time when it might bring solace to my soul in difficult circumstances.

Although the sun was shining, the air was cold and I shivered and turned up the collar of my coat to protect me from the wind. Winter had certainly arrived at these high altitudes in Kingdom Park.
"Will it always be so cold?" I asked, "I don't think I could stand cold like this all the time!"

The Master handed me a cloak. It felt soft and light, yet warm, like cashmere wool. It had been woven in my favourite shade of light blue, reached down almost to my feet and had a hood attached. Almost instantly, I began to feel warm and turned to ask the Master why this should be so. He answered my question before I asked it.
"The cloak is made of my Love – hold it tightly around you in this season – it will bring warmth and comfort to your soul."

He then produced some walking boots and two poles and indicated that I should take them. I did so rather reluctantly because the boots were big and ugly looking, not at all like my usual footwear and I couldn't see why I had to carry two thin poles.

"Sit down for a moment," the Master instructed me, "and let Me explain a little about Winter."

I did so quickly, realising that I had displeased Him in some way by my reluctance.

"I'm not going to lie to you," He said slowly, choosing His words carefully. "Winter is the hardest season in Kingdom Park but remember that you were able to find joy and beauty in Autumn and you will find joy and beauty in Winter too. Going through a Winter Season comes to everyone in Kingdom Park and some go through many such seasons in their lives. At some time, of course, you will walk in your final Winter Season."

"That's what I'm most fearful of," I whispered. "I'm not going to know if the Winter I'm walking through is my final one or not and I've always feared the unknown."

"Little one," He assured me, "you don't have to be afraid. Take a look at the road you have walked."

I looked back and realised that because we were standing near the top of the mountain, I could see the whole journey I had made from the cross-shaped gate – the hills I had climbed, the valleys I had walked through, the rivers I had crossed, the twists and turns the path had taken.

"Haven't I been with you all the time?" He asked. "Have I ever abandoned you? Can't you trust Me to complete the journey with you? Do you think I would make you walk the hardest part alone?"

I pulled the soft cloak of His Love tighter to me and felt its warmth envelop me and I knew deep in my heart a calm assurance that He would be with me right to the end.

"Now," He said, "let Me explain about the boots and the poles. The Father and I know that it's not easy to walk through Winter. The snow is deep and the path is often unclear. The boots might be big but they will help you to walk in difficult places."

As I put them on I noticed a label inside each boot. It contained just one word "Faith".

"Step out in your Faith boots," the Master encouraged and as I walked on to the deep snow, I discovered that my boots gave me a sense of security and safety. I realised very quickly that I had to walk differently – planting my feet in their Faith boots very firmly into the snow – and soon I was making progress so I began to walk a little faster.

That was when I realised that not only did I have to walk differently – I would have to walk slowly! My feet slipped on an icy patch and down I tumbled. I had been afraid of falling in case I hurt myself but hadn't realised that the snow would cushion my fall. It was rather like falling into a cold feather duvet.

The Master quickly reached out and helped me to my feet.

"That's what the poles are for!" He laughed. "You're not meant to just carry them, you're meant to use them to support you as you walk."

I looked at them again and saw that, like the Faith boots, they too had labels – Patience and Perseverance.

"These are the Father's gifts to you for the Winter Season. If you plant your poles firmly into the snow, they will support you and help you to walk more easily."

And so, slowly but surely, we made our way up the steep snow-covered mountain side. It wasn't an easy journey and many times I thought with longing of the days in Spring and Summer when I had been able to run, singing, along the path. I found that my legs got tired walking in the deep snow and many times I had to use my poles of Patience and Perseverance to keep my feet from slipping.

Often when it seemed that I just couldn't go on, we arrived at a resting place – how grateful I was for those little log cabins built by pilgrims who had followed this path before. How strong they must have been to have climbed through the hard Winter Season and still found time and energy to make provision for those who would follow them.

It was so good to shelter from the biting wind for a while and enjoy the provisions they had left behind – water from the Spirit reservoir and sweetmeats from the Father's kitchen. And for a few moments I experienced the joy that the Master had promised for this season. I could see the beauty He had spoken of from every window in the cabin – majestic mountains that stretched far into the distance, amazing waterfalls etching out paths to the nearest rivers, serene lakes glistening in the valleys below. What refreshment for the soul – each time we stopped to rest the beauty seemed to give me courage to face the challenge of the next stage in this arduous trek through the Winter Season.

The Master and I had been walking for many days and although the path had been difficult to follow, the skies had been blue and the sun had shone. Then, late one afternoon, the clouds gathered and the sky darkened and the temperature dropped even lower. A cold northerly wind whipped round the side of the mountain. It tugged at my warm cloak of Love and I had to hold on to it very tightly. Then the snow began to fall.

At first I was entranced by the hypnotic effect of the white flakes falling all around me but soon I began to feel afraid as the snow fell faster and the flakes grew bigger. It got more and more difficult to walk against the fierce icy wind and I kept checking my Faith boots anxiously, scared that they might leak and no longer protect me. I leaned so hard on my poles of Patience and Perseverance that I thought they would snap beneath the strain.

The storm grew so fierce that I lost sight of the Master.
"Where are You?" I cried out in fear and desperation. "I can't see You any more."

At that moment I lost my footing and fell head first into a deep snow drift. The snow seemed to close in around me so that I could hardly breathe. My lungs felt as though they were on fire and I could feel my heart pounding in my chest. My arms flailed about wildly and my legs kicked aimlessly in every direction but no matter how hard I tried, I couldn't work out how to get out of the snowdrift.

"Maybe this is it," I thought, resigning myself to the inevitable, "maybe this is my final Winter Season….. maybe this is how it all ends……. desperate, lonely and with no sight of the Master."

Then all at once, I felt a familiar touch on my back and the Master drew me out to stand once more at His side, shivering and bedraggled but safe!

"I won't leave you," He promised. "I can reach you even in the deepest snowdrift or in the fiercest storm. You may not see Me clearly but I'll be there."

Ashamed to have doubted Him, I dusted off the snow, took up my poles again and set out once more. The storm had stopped and the sky had cleared.

"We'll soon be there," the Master said. How relieved I felt. Maybe my Winter Season would soon be over. We crested a ridge and the Master indicated that I should stop.

"This is what I wanted you to see," He said. "Just watch with me for a while."

I was glad to rest and leaned on my walking poles as I gazed at the scene before me. A great white expanse stretched far into the distance – a gently sloping snowfield. Skiers were taking advantage of the freshly fallen snow and the air was filled with shouts of laughter and the swish of skis.

The Master smiled at my look of amazement.

"Yes," He said, "there can be fun in the Winter Season. Now keep watching and tell me what you see."

I wasn't sure what I was meant to see but stood patiently and observed all that was happening on the mountain slope. A young competent skier waved his ski pole in greeting as he whizzed past me and disappeared into the distance. My eyes followed the parallel lines of his skis marked out in the snow and I realised that he had gone right down the mountainside to the lower slopes in the valley. In that area young families were learning to ski together – skiing a little way, losing balance, laughing as they fell over in the soft snow. I looked at the Master, sensing that there was something to learn.

"Have you noticed that there are no learners at this altitude?" He asked. "The Father won't let you journey through the Winter Season until you have learnt how to cope."

"Where did the skier go?" I enquired, then suddenly remembered what else I had seen.

"Oh," I exclaimed, "he's gone into another Spring, hasn't he? Where the snow was melting, the grass was growing again and I think I saw leaves on the trees…………….. That's why he was so happy – his Winter Season is over!"

The Master smiled and nodded His assent.

"Keep watching," He urged, "there is more to learn."

I watched a few other skiers as they sped down to the edge of the snowfield and my heart was filled with hope. Maybe my own Winter Season would soon be at an end and I too would speed down the mountain to walk once more on paths bordered by snowdrops and crocuses – into a new Springtime.

I lifted my gaze again and this time watched those who were skiing across the mountainside towards the far horizon. They were proceeding at a more sedate pace and some seemed to be finding the going tough, stopping often to lean on their ski poles to rest. I wondered aloud if their ski poles were also labelled Patience and Perseverance, like the walking poles that had been such a help to me in my journey.

"Some of them need Patience and Perseverance," the Master said in reply, "but others are leaning on poles called Courage or Promise or Endurance. The skis have names too – they are called Praise and Prayer. Learn well how to use them on the Nursery slopes and they will enable you to cross the great snowfields with ease."

I thought of my faltering attempts on the gentle slopes when I had first been introduced to skis and determined that if I ever made it through this harsh Winter, I would return to those slopes and practise using Praise and Prayer – I knew now how valuable they would be in another Winter Season.

"What else do you see?" asked the Master gently.

I watched a little longer as the skiers made their way towards the far horizon and it seemed to me as though a fine curtain of falling snow hung across the sky. Each skier formed his own track in the fresh snow and as they approached the veil of snow, they seemed to lean forwards on their skis as though in anticipation. Just before they entered the snow veil, each one in turn threw away his snow poles, raised his arms in the air as though in worship and glided gracefully into the curtain.

I turned to the Master with tears in my eyes.

"Oh now I understand," I whispered, "this is their final Winter……… there's nothing to fear after all……….. the Father's House is behind the snow veil, isn't it?"

"Yes child," He replied, "the Father's House and the Eternal Spring I told you about. You asked why everything has to fade and die – that's the reason. In Kingdom Park, death is merely a passing through a veil from this kingdom to the Father's House, from Winter to Eternal Spring."

"What is it like on the other side of the snow veil?" I asked with longing in my heart.

"Too wonderful for you to imagine," He laughed and the longing deepened at the sound of His laughter, "Beauty beyond this Kingdom's most beautiful, majesty that will far outshine snow-capped mountains, the unimaginable sound of the singing of angels and the worship of saints...................... and the glory......... oh the glory..........."

I looked into His face as His voice tailed off and what I saw there brought the ache of longing back into my heart for it seemed, as the light of His countenance shone upon me, that I had caught a tiny glimpse of that glory in His face.

It was enough! Winter would hold no fear for me now. I would carry that single glimpse of the glory to come, through every Winter Season, until that day when with arms raised high in worship, I would slip through the snow veil and enter the unimaginable delights of Eternal Spring in the Presence of the King.

SHOW ME YOUR FACE

God of all Glory
God of all Grace
Come by Your Spirit,
Show me Your face.
Only a glimpse, Lord
The tiniest glance
Would give me such joy,
Would make my heart dance.
A few rays of splendour,
To fall on my eyes,
A sprinkling of wisdom
From God Only Wise.
A moment of might,
A hint of Your power,
Your mercy like raindrops,
Your love like a shower.
Just pull back the veil, Lord
Meet me now in this place,
Surround with Your Glory
Lord, show me Your face.

THE END